The NHS – life and dea
you see? Maria Adams h
from the bottom to the to
the brink. How one pers.. .... so much on her way up,
but never allowed her care for others to suffer, always
demanding excellence whatever the obstacles, and there have
been many along the way. This book is a true account of what
was encountered during 45 years. The bullying, fear, double
standards and disturbing behaviours can be shocking to read
but these events are true and captured in the pages of this
book. There are some light moments which will make you
smile along with those which are darker. The pandemic took
the NHS to another level, the likes of which we never want to
see again.

Maria Adams

BEHIND THE MASK I WEAR

AUSTIN MACAULEY PUBLISHERS™

LONDON • CAMBRIDGE • NEW YORK • SHARJAH

A CIP catalogue record for this title is available from the British Library.

ISBN 9781035836444 (Paperback)
ISBN 9781035836451 (ePub e-book)

www.austinmacauley.co.uk

First Published 2024
Austin Macauley Publishers Ltd®
1 Canada Square
Canary Wharf
London
E14 5AA

First and foremost, I want to thank all the amazing patients and staff I have worked with over the years. I also want to thank the not so amazing people who made my life a living hell at the time but helped make me the person I am today. My amazing husband, Will, and daughter, Rebecca have been my rocks and supported everything I have ever done. Thank you, I love you both.

This book has been written with love for the NHS that I have worked in for more than 40 years. It is a true and accurate account of one of our most treasured possessions. As British people, we are proud of what it represents and those who work within it. It has been and still is the envy of the world; it surely is a true gem.

The issues described in this book are totally true but I have changed names, places and any other facts, which may bring attention to individuals or organisations to protect anonymity, this however does not change the facts and what has happened along the way.

It shows just one person's journey through the sometimes turbulent and challenging times and how it affected her own life and well-being, having to deal with so many issues during one career and still maintaining passion and the highest standards, never faltering from her own beliefs and morals.

There are some dark areas of our beloved NHS and this book will portray it in its chapters. There are issues which will surprise you, some may even shock you, but the fact remains, these have happened and can't be changed. The NHS has changed so much over the years and in many areas, not for the better.

So, I hope you enjoy reading this and I am going to enjoy writing it. I am sure I will laugh, cry and reflect so much whilst doing so. I do write under an alias to also protect those who may be associated with me.

Chapter One

As a young girl, I was always the one who wanted to look after everyone. If someone was ill, I would be there and try to help. I seemed to love blood and gore but always wanted to care and make things better. My parents were hardworking people who instilled a strong work ethic into my sister, Lisa and myself. We were taught from an early age to be strong, stick to our beliefs and always be honest and truthful – something I carried through life with me.

I did really well in school and gained six A levels with nine O levels and was destined for a career in medicine. I applied to a well-known London School of Medicine and was accepted. I was overjoyed and so excited. I had met Will when I was 16 and we were inseparable. Will was not an academic and was a practical lad who had his heart fixed on a trade as an electrician but equally wanted the best for me.

I didn't consider that we would not be together when I went to medical school and we continued to be together all the time. Our families thought we were joined at the hip; we were very happy. I prepared for my much-awaited medical school place and worked in Clark's shoe shop whilst I was waiting to go. I had planned it and was almost fully packed; that's how excited I was.

At around 6 months before going to medical school, I found out I was going to be a mother. This changed everything; I was, to say the least, shocked as I was taking the contraceptive pill and took it like clockwork. Will and I married, not because of our baby, but because we wanted to be together and it was a natural progression as far as we were concerned.

There was no way I would not have my baby, so decided to defer my place, hoping in the future, I could still take it up. The dean asked me to go to see him. I was nervous but thought this is a good thing; he wants to advise me on what to do next and how long to wait.

I arrived at the dean's office with Will. I was around 7 months pregnant at this time and he came out to get me and told Will to stay where he was. He said I was irresponsible, and really, medicine wouldn't be for me as I was going to probably have many children and my career would be short and wasted.

There was a distinct lack of compassion in the way he dealt with my delicate situation and knew how devastated I was. He was obviously not interested in anything I had to say and, in fact, showed no interest in me as a person. I was flabbergasted and upset and thinking is this the way medicine would be and the NHS in the future?

I felt so deflated and almost unworthy; that's how he made me feel. I left his office in floods of tears and didn't know what my future held as in a career. Will was there to support me through this and although he was angry at me, being treated in this way never said anything which would have inflamed the situation.

We went home and settled into our life together. I always felt something had been taken from me and deep in my heart I was grieving for this but didn't voice or show this to anyone. I felt cheated of what was my passion in life. I kept up the appearance of not bothering for months and no one knew how I was really feeling my heart was broken.

We continued being a happy duo and thoughts of medicine were still on my mind but Braxton hick's contractions (practice contractions getting ready for labour) and the fear of labour and motherhood at a young age overtook this. I had a good pregnancy, except I was the size of a small country and was a bit low on iron, which I had to endure regular iron injections when the tablets weren't working. A small price to pay for a healthy mum and baby.

I was induced into labour at 40 weeks as my blood pressure was going up. I remember being sat upright in the bed with long blonde plaits down to my waist and a lovely midwife coming in and holding my hand, knowing how afraid I was.

She sat by the side of me. Those days, sitting on the bed just wasn't allowed, and talked me through everything. She was amazing and at that time something inside me said, 'Right, lady, when you're ready, you're going to be a nurse.' I had a lightbulb moment.

I had an easy labour by most people's standards and gave birth to my beautiful daughter at almost 9 pounds in weight. Will wasn't allowed in the delivery room but paced up and down outside with his friend and I know he wanted to be there with me. My world had changed at this point as I looked down at my beautiful baby.

We all went home to our flat and I started to see how different health professionals were and by just being understanding and listening to how it can change someone's day. In came Sister Riley, a midwife, with no filter and in fact no tact or decorum.

Firstly, she almost threw me across the kitchen table to insert suppositories into me; no warning was given, so it came as one almighty shock. Her communication was almost non-existent and when she did speak, it was in short bursts, which made it difficult as I felt I couldn't ask her anything. Then she had me in what felt like a wrestling hold to look at my stitches. Again, I'm sure she had a mean streak in her that no one else possessed.

I was trying so hard to breastfeed and was very sore with cracked nipples which were bleeding. She was so rough making the baby 'latch on' to me. I was crying in pain as she squeezed my full breasts in a vice-like grip. I didn't want her touching my baby but she had to do so and I felt she had no compassion for the tiny bundle just tossing her around like a rag doll. It left me so distraught.

Will got home from work and saw me distressed and stated, 'She's not coming in here again. I will be here tomorrow when she turns up and will send her packing.' The next day, thankfully, a different midwife came who was chatty and had a different approach completely, so normality seemed to be restored. I didn't ever see Sister Riley again, which I was pleased about.

Rebecca was 3 months old and I wanted to look at my options for a future career. I just knew that my life would not be fulfilled unless I worked in healthcare. I saw an advert in the local press for the major teaching hospital nearby for a trainee cardiographer. I looked up in a medical dictionary what this was and found it was taking ECGs (electrocardiograms) from patients to look at how their heart health was. I decided to apply.

I had forgotten all about it until a letter arrived asking me to attend an interview. I hadn't told Will about applying, so plucked up the courage to do so. Don't know why I was worried about telling him. He was supportive as always and said, 'That's fine. Go and see what it's about and then we will sort out the childcare. We had two sets of supportive parents, so really needn't worry.'

The day of the interview came around and I dressed appropriately; demure and sedate. I sat there waiting and another girl arrived. She was very confident and dressed in a bright pink short mini dress. I can still see it vividly in my mind now. She said, 'Hi, I'm Suzie. Are you here for the job?'

We started a conversation and she was so much more confident than I was. Even though she had no experience. A small man with grey hair and a moustache came out introducing himself as Gavin, head of the department, and took Suzie in with him. I could see him looking at her legs and the low-cut dress she had on gave a bird's-eye view of her ample cleavage.

In fact, she was tall and statuesque. His eyes came in line with her breasts so he certainly enjoyed the view. As he ushered her in, I noticed the way he walked really close up beside her, which I thought was slightly creepy.

She came out again with him, all smiles, and I noticed his hand around her waist as they were talking. I then thought, *Well, this is pointless. I'm not going to stand a chance.* He called my name. I stood up and I was slightly taller than he was and he again was eyeing me up and down. He commented on my eyes, saying how lovely and blue they were and what beautiful long hair I had.

He ushered me into the interview room and I felt his hand low down my back. I was a bit uneasy, to say the least. There were another two people in the room for the interview and I felt better knowing there was some form of protection. It went well and I was told to wait outside. Suzie was waiting there also along with 2 others that I hadn't seen but had been interviewed.

We were called in one at a time. The first two didn't get the job so left. Then Suzie went in and came back out grinning, telling me she was sorry but she got it. Not sorry at all, I would have said. She then left. I went back in and was also offered a job. I was elated and would be starting in 1 month. I was on my road to a career in the NHS. My dreams were starting to be fulfilled.

Will and I soon sorted baby care and I was relieved knowing grandparents would look after Rebecca always.

The day came around to start my new career. I donned the snow-white dress and my sensible lace-up shoes and turned up for my first day. I sat waiting and Suzie walked in and her face was a picture!

'What are you doing here?' she growled.

'Same as you, I guess,' was my answer.

She had taken up her white uniform, so it resembled a mini dress and the way she wore it was more fashion statement than professional. I really did not go for the same look as her. It was quite outrageous. We were never going to be friends, that was clear. She was someone who was always trying to score points and I am not a competitive person, so I let her get on with it.

After a few months of being in the post, I went into our coffee room earlier than usual to find her and the head of the department in a compromising position where he had his hand in an inappropriate place, up under her dress and she was allowing him to do it. I could not quite believe what I saw. They quickly moved apart and he asked, 'What are you doing here?'

It was a communal coffee room, so I had come for a coffee break. He started to try to be friendly, asking if I wanted a coffee. I said I was fine. I left the room. I didn't quite know what to do. Suzie was 22 years old and he was 54 years old – a married man with a family. I know that they were having an affair and things continued to happen in various places and often after work in his office when everyone had gone home.

It was obvious except to Gavin that Suzie was playing him to get what she wanted. He, on the other hand, was getting what he wanted, so would keep her sweet. Suzie got promoted by him after 9 months. It wasn't for her efficiency at her work, that was for sure. This was my first experience of the NHS casting couch and by no means the last!

I used to watch the nurses on the wards and think I so want to do this. I wanted to be more involved with the patients and care for them, so I applied for nurse training in the February 1975. I was invited to interview and was advised, as I had a small child, the enrolled nurse training would be better for me, less stressful.

I agreed. Even though I had enough O and A levels to go to medical school, all I wanted to do was care for others. The principal of the nursing school was a large softly spoken lady who had 3 children herself so knew how difficult it was to bring up children. She offered me a place there and then to start in the June of that year. I was thrilled. It was what I wanted so badly.

Will was really pleased for me and his job allowed him to be at home slightly more to enable me to increase my hours and cope with shifts. I gave my notice to leave in the April of that year. How I kept the secret I will never know as I was so very excited. Suzie, who was then in a more senior position, stated that she thought it was the best for me as I seemed to be very patient-orientated. *It certainly was a strange comment*, I thought, *why are we here and who for?*

I left the post understanding more about the heart, which in my opinion was a bonus and it was always a help to learn and I was thirsty for knowledge and took every opportunity to ask questions and push myself to understand everything I encountered.

I turned up to my nurse training, nervous but excited. I was one of 28 in the group with just 1 male who was the best person you could meet and we became such good friends. He was already a father of older children and changed his career from being an engineer as he had enough of it. I became friends with Judith and she and I shared the same sense of humour and loved to have fun but this was our passion and our dream.

There were two girls who had already done an orthopaedic pre-nursing course; one who seemed so confident and was constantly giving us all advice. I later found out most of it was to make herself popular but that was taken with a pinch of salt. We were taken to get our uniforms and met

Sister Tucker, the 'linen sister'. She was a sour-faced woman who resembled someone from a carry-on film.

She took us in groups of 4 and asked us all to go to the big changing room and strip down to our bras and knickers to get measured. I have never been shy but the others were mortified. She came in and was clearly enjoying what she saw. She slowly measured each one of us and you felt her hand gliding over your breasts and across the pubic area when measuring our hips.

I kept my eyes firmly on her. She was happy in her work, which in this case wasn't a good thing. You did feel violated by this awful woman but there were worse things to come which I would find out later in my career.

I had a great time as a pupil nurse, as we were called and most of the time I was happy. I loved to learn and soaked up every detail I possibly could and spent time ensuring I understood everything I was told. I did have many sad times, particularly when you got close to patients and they deteriorated or passed away, this was hard to take on board sometimes and never so much as on the children's ward.

Sister Potter was 4'8" tall and ruled with a rod of iron. Most of the children were as tall as her but she was the most incredible role model. She adored the children and the parents and had an almost childlike way about her. She didn't have children of her own or had ever been married but every child that came onto the ward was like they were her own.

We had a beautiful little girl on the ward with a rare syndrome and she was being fed by a tube. Abigail was a beautiful child whose eyes followed you but she didn't move her little head. You could feel her look penetrating into you; it was quite chilling at first. Abigail was always in a bouncy chair within a large cot so she could see her surroundings; this to try to stimulate her.

Sister Potter took me in to teach me how to do the feeds and the love and care she gave to this dying child was like nothing I had ever seen. She passed away whilst I was on the ward, aged just 16 months old. I found this so very hard, especially as a mother of a young child myself. Sister Potter was so caring and sat and cried with me and the parents and wouldn't go home until everyone appeared to be more settled. She was one in a million and totally dedicated to her career or was it a calling?

Whilst a 'learner', you moved around frequently usually anywhere between four and twelve weeks, so you gained as much experience as possible.

I then moved wards and met an incredible staff nurse named Jane. She was on a cardiac unit which had intensive care beds and this woman had so much knowledge. The doctors used to ask her what to do and what she thought. I was in awe of her. I was useful and felt pleased that my previous cardiographer skills could be used.

Jane was a fantastic teacher and I felt that my learning was increasing every time I was with her; just watching her was inspiring. My first injection is something I will always remember vividly. It was going to be deep into a man's thigh for pain relief. He had had his leg run over by a train so was in extreme pain.

As I put the needle deep into his muscle, looking at Jane for reassurance, he was crying like a small child. I was so upset that I thought I had hurt him. I started to cry too. Jane put a reassuring hand on my shoulder and said softly, '*No, Maria, you are helping him. The crying is from his dreadful leg injuries. Come back in 15 minutes and see him then, you will see.* That really helped my confidence but not my makeup.

I did go back and see the patient. He was resting quietly free of pain. I made up my mind that I wanted to be like Jane, an exceptional nurse, that was my aim. Jane would spring into action when one of the heart monitors gave out the alarm for an abnormal rhythm and her calmness had an effect on everyone. She was always in control of the situation and even the most experienced doctor wanted Jane around and to take the helm. Her abilities were amazing to watch.

We were now moving around wards every 8–12 weeks to gain experience in all types of nursing and conditions. It was a good thing for our education but often you got on so well on a ward, you were sad to leave and there were times when the speciality just wasn't for you. That was par for the course and accepted across the board.

I then worked in a neurological ward where I met a young woman who had only been married for 6 months and developed a brain infection after falling into a river, which was highly inhabited by rats and developed Weils disease (a form of bacterial infection which is found in water contaminated by urine from rats or cattle).

Marion was just 25 years old and was in a coma but did have bouts where she looked as if she knew what was going on around her for a short time. Her husband, Derek, was with her most of the time but was always trying to strike up a conversation with the staff. He didn't appear to want to talk to Marion. He constantly looked bored and there wasn't any contact or hand holding. I noticed this very quickly.

I came on for a late shift and I went about my duties. Derek was sitting on the bed of another patient when I went to take Marion's observations and he came over when he saw me there. He was particularly touchy-feely with others and he put his arm around me, saying he had missed me as I had days off. I tried to pull away, making excuses for not standing close to him. I felt very uneasy.

I went into the kitchen and as I was getting jugs of water ready for the patients, he came in and closed the door. He asked me if I liked him, which I thought was very odd. I said I like everyone and tried to change the subject. He walked towards me and I wasn't sure what to do. I raised my voice saying you need to go back to your wife as I am sure if you sat and talked to her; it would be a great comfort to you both.

He was still coming close to me and I was frightened of him. He was a big man and wasn't sure what he was about to do. He lunged forward to try to kiss me and I screamed and threw a jug of water all over him. He wasn't happy and was standing over me. The kitchen door flew open and in came the staff nurse.

Derek said that I just threw the water over him for no reason! I started to protest and was told to be quiet and go to the office. I was shaking and crying with fright. The staff nurse came in and said what on earth was I thinking. I tried to explain but she wasn't accepting of the true account and said I must have led him on.

I was totally shocked as so many had noticed his creepy ways with female staff. The staff nurse angrily said to me maybe if you weren't blond with big blue eyes this wouldn't have happened. You most likely think all men want you. Women like you shouldn't be a nurse. I couldn't believe what I was hearing. I had done nothing wrong but was being blamed for being who I was.

She had never had a boyfriend and I believe never ever did she was a sour woman who was always sniping at the other female nurses when she was in charge. I didn't hear anything else on the matter, only to be told that some husbands try to find a substitute when wives become ill and I should have been more understanding of him.

I kept my distance and tried not to be the one looking after Marion or at least be with another nurse when I did. I never entered into eye contact or conversation with Derek, as always afraid of what he would do or accuse me of. Sadly, Marion passed away after contracting pneumonia about 6 weeks after this incident and I never saw Derek again.

Whilst on the neurological unit, I also cared for a gentleman from overseas who was from an exclusive family who were extremely affluent and influential where they were from. He had a serious accident whilst in the UK and his family chose for him to come to the unit, as it was renowned for excellent care.

He had been there 6 months with little sign of any improvement, which was devastating for his family. His brother visited every week and asked me if I would like to come to be his private nurse back where they lived. He offered me a huge salary. I had to decline but thanked him for his kind offer. What he was offering I wouldn't earn in years. He used to bring me gifts of perfume and chocolates, which I always said I was unable to take but he insisted.

I had to give them to the ward sister who distributed them to everyone. We didn't want to insult the family. It was very difficult but we weren't allowed to accept gifts. The patient went to a nursing home and died 10 years later. He and his family left a lasting impact on me for the closeness and love they all shared and the gratitude they showed to us all.

I was seconded to a (then called) geriatric hospital and the ward was large and spacious and the patients were well-cared for. One day I was given the task of baths with a nursing auxiliary named Jean. In those days, you were allocated tasks rather than patients, so you didn't get to care for the person as a whole. There were books for everything, it seemed. The bath book had columns where you had to tick what you had done, cut toes or fingernails, washed hair, etc. There were bowel and teeth books. You name it and there seemed to be a book!

We had had an admission overnight of a lady who was a recluse and had not washed or changed her clothes in what was believed to be years. I don't know exactly the length of time but the strong odour of urine and dirt was unbearable. We had a special bathroom for ulcers of the legs and took Mabel in here.

We couldn't get her stockings off so decided to soak them off along with most of her clothes, as it was all stuck fast to her skin. The warm bubble bath would help with the removal and as we were watching the water, we could see what looked like "activity" in the water. On close inspection, it was maggots that came out of her legs from within the ulcers. We both felt quite unwell at this point.

At the end of the bath Mabel's legs were almost depleted of flesh the poor woman must have been in agony. How on earth this happened, I will never know as no one bothered with her and she had no family. It was a long road ahead for Mabel to get some rehabilitation.

We then started on the long list of baths and we are talking general chit chat and just finished with one lady and Jean had taken her back to her bed. I was cleaning the bath before the next one. Jean came back in and closed the door. The room was hot, so I asked her to open the door but she didn't. I went to walk past her to open it myself and she made a grab for my breast.

I shouted at her. I was in shock. The door flew open and in ran another student nurse who, apparently, Jean had done the same thing to a few weeks before. Jean pushed past both of us and ran off. We had to give statements but we never knew if Jean was spoken to about the incident, as she was back at work on another ward a month later. Her brother was the charge nurse (the male equivalent of the ward sister) on the unit, so we are unsure of what happened.

We felt disgusted by the situation and felt disbelieved as she had worked there for 10 years. So how many more had it happened to and were they too afraid to say anything?

There seemed to be a culture of fear generally at this time and it was widespread. We were warned it wouldn't be in anyone's best interest to make an issue. We felt warned off in a bullying way, which was unnerving, especially to a mere trainee nurse. This was my first experience of "closing ranks" and it was quite shocking as truth and justice was what I expected, in my mind, I thought this would be the case, very naïve of me, to say the least.

I was beginning to think there was something wrong with me and I took a long look in the mirror. I couldn't help the way I looked. I didn't flaunt myself. I was quiet and quite sedate at this stage in my life but I was encountering some awful situations. At this point I questioned why I was doing this job.

I worked on a surgical ward with another sister who was so unpredictable. It was almost hilarious. She would do whatever she thought was right at the time even if it wasn't. The consultants would shout at her, she would shout back and it was a battle of wills at times. Her patients loved her but her skills and judgement were questionable.

At times, she was downright dangerous but again, nothing ever came of any of her shenanigans. She called everyone darling. No exceptions and never listened to a word anyone said. When you asked her a question, she replied usually 'do what you want!'

There was also an extremely dangerous staff nurse named Eunice. She was tall with thick black out-of-control eyebrows and a tight brown perm. She used to make all her own clothes, mostly out of her mother's curtains, she proclaimed. I had witnessed some practice which was totally out of order but this particular day was potentially lethal.

A patient had returned from the operating theatre and needed a blood transfusion. She had put the bag containing the blood up on the stand and then went off to do the drug round. I was feeding a patient opposite and sat in view of her administering medicines. She had to draw up some antibiotics which needed to go directly into the vein (intravenous) of the patient with the blood transfusion.

I saw her take the syringe and go to inject it into the bag of whole blood being transfused! I jumped off my chair not even thinking and grabbed the syringe from her. 'What are you doing?' I said.

She looked at me in disbelief. It is a well-known fact that nothing is ever added to a blood transfusion even a lowly pupil nurse had this knowledge. I had to stop her from doing anything like this ever again as someone could die as a result of her incompetence.

I spoke with the nursing officer on duty who was equally as horrified. Eunice was demoted and not allowed to deliver medicines again, as it wasn't the first time there had been a serious incident. I wasn't happy reporting a colleague but knew patients need protecting.

The training went quickly for 2 years and I qualified and went to work in a hospital closer to home. I worked in oncology for 6 months and learnt some amazing skills but also found that the work wasn't for me as I wasn't able to switch off when I left so became quite depressed as there was so much bad news.

I didn't have the right to feel like that when others were suffering pain and terminal illness but I didn't know how not to feel this way. I had to deal with death on so many levels from young to old and in most cases these patients were so sick for such a long time it was harrowing seeing the suffering of not only the patients but their relatives, day after day seeing their precious loved ones, knowing they wouldn't recover.

Most nights on my way home I would cry as I felt helpless. Many of my friends and colleagues said they went through similar feelings when working in this environment. It took a toll on me so felt I wasn't giving my best to those who needed it so started to look for something different.

I then moved onto a surgical ward; it was so very busy – 35 beds with a great team of staff. Sister Shutts was a tall attractive ex-forces nurse who was good, fun and always visible to us and the patients. We also had a young nursing officer who we were all petrified of as she did spot-check ward rounds with you and if you didn't know your patients you were mincemeat.

I remember writing little anecdotes on the inside of my white starched apron in case she picked me and she did often as I was always the mischievous one or so I was told.

I was doing a set of nights and I was working with Trevor – one of our staff nurses and 2 other auxiliaries. We had a table where we sat in the middle of the ward so we could see all around. The ward was Nightingale style (long ward with beds lined up on either side). Trevor was known to be a bit of a Mr Bean character so we were always on our guard.

It was the early hours of the morning and Trevor said, looking at Mr Brown walking back from the bathroom, 'He's going to trip on his dressing gown cord if he's not careful.'

I looked up from what I was doing to realise it wasn't his cord but his intestines as his wound had burst (a burst abdomen is rare and usually occurs after major abdominal surgery where the sutures don't hold). I jumped up and got him back to his bed before he collapsed. Trevor is still looking and wondering what on earth I am doing as he hadn't tripped!

I was trying to be quiet as everyone was sleeping but shouting quietly doesn't work. I needed saline and swabs to cover his abdomen and to fast bleep the on-call to get here quickly. It was a tense situation. Mr Brown went back to the theatre but sadly passed away through infection several days later.

Losing a patient is never easy and dealing not only with your own thoughts, especially when you have developed a fondness for the patient but to help the family in their grief.

One Sunday, I remember it so well, I was on duty and we had just dished up the Sunday lunches from the big steel trolley which was wheeled up with freshly cooked wholesome food 3 times per day and the nurses served it and ensured everyone got what they wanted as well as ate properly.

We always took it in turns to have our food too from the trolley but only what was left over and after all patients had theirs, it smelt so good and tasted great too. We actually weren't allowed to do it but hey, we liked to live dangerously.

That particular day we made the mistake of letting our own Mr Bean, Trevor dish up lunch and what a mistake that was! He put chocolate sauce all over the roast lamb, thinking it was gravy; it did look similar but smelt completely different. Disaster for the first 6 patients!

It was my turn to go and have my lunch and I was pretty hungry. I gathered it up and disappeared into the larder in the huge kitchen on the ward, closing the door behind me. The larder was really big. I put my plate on the shelf and started to attack the food, almost shovelling it in as I knew I had to be quick.

I had a mouth rammed full of roast potatoes, carrots and peas and the door flew open and the severe nursing officer stood glaring at me. I was stunned and all I could think of saying was 'Would you like some?'

Where that came from I don't know. She turned on her heels and walked away, not saying a thing. Trevor saw her walking out and asked why was she laughing? I saw her in a completely different light after this.

Cora was a new auxiliary and a sweet naïve girl who was Trevor in the female form. She was asked on her late shift to organise the denture round, which was giving new denture pots to the patients so their teeth can be cleaned. Cora started the round and we noticed that she was getting the pot with the dentures straight back and writing on the lids which was where we found the patient's name and bed number.

Great, that's good practice, we thought. What we didn't realise is she then took all the pots out into the sluice and tipped them into one big bowl so everyone's teeth were mixed up but the names were on the pots! It took a lot of sorting out by an emergency dentist as no one could eat!

Another great achievement of Cora was the sputum pot round. Yes, every bed had a sputum pot in those days which was changed daily – many full of the most disgusting slimy phlegm of various colours. She had collected at least 25 pots and pushing the large glass-topped flat trolley down the ward hit the side of a bed sending the content of every single pot hurtling into the air and landing over the back of a visitor.

The poor woman was beside herself. She let out a huge scream and started to wail uncontrollably. We came out to see her left dripping in foul gunk. Cora soon went to work in the hospital shop and away from harm although I did hear she switched off the freezers in her first week and all the ice cream and ice lollies went to mush.

The ward rounds were stuffy affairs and the sister always had to be there because the consultant demanded it. Mr Winton, a rotund stern man with huge eyebrows, came into the ward, white coat flowing behind him because he couldn't do it up. A string of brown-nosed juniors running behind him. He was a big cheese and a great eminent surgeon who was good at what he did but very judgemental.

My first observation was of a young woman with abdominal pain thought to be appendicitis, brought in by ambulance. He had stopped at the bottom of her bed and looked at her notes, not saying a word to her. He pulled at the bottom of the bedclothes, lifting it up to look at her feet.

'Salpingitis,' he roared, 'she has painted toenails, a sure sign.' (salpingitis is an inflammation of the fallopian tubes usually from infection). He actually was right on this occasion but not a clinical sign I must emphasise!

I happened to be in charge of the ward and he ignored me as he blustered past. He stopped at the first bed and put his hand out for the notes and I passed them to him. No words were exchanged between the 2 of us and, in fact, he didn't even look in my direction. I was becoming extremely fed up with being ignored. We got to bed 15 and he put his hand out and I didn't respond. He started to wave it around, still not speaking.

He turned and looked at me saying, 'What is wrong with you, girl? I am not standing here as an ornament. Just give me the notes!'

All the brown noses were wincing and nodding in my direction as though I had committed murder. I saw red. "Mr Winton," I said in a loud voice. "I am not here to be treated like a child, nor am I here as your slave so kindly speak to me and give me credit for being a professional and a human being!"

I felt my face throb with heat and my heart was racing. He looked at me over his half-rimmed specs and said, "My my, young woman, you have a backbone. I admire that in an individual I want you on my side when we go into battle, that's for sure."

I was flabbergasted. The remainder of the ward round was a much more civil affair with my contribution being acknowledged and a big thank you at the end. Result! My bubble burst when I was reprimanded by the surgical floor sister for having the audacity to speak to a surgeon in this way if I carried on this way, I would never work in the city again or for that matter anywhere else.

I couldn't believe the Dickensian attitude of this narrow-minded woman who hated the thought of anyone getting on if you had another life outside of the hospital and nursing. She knew I was married with a child and said it was wrong to another nurse who loved to stir things up and made a point of letting me know. It was a shame that as nurses we didn't seem to stick together and have each other's backs but preferred to stab each other in the back. This was apparent early on.

I continued in the job and loved it. There were always the hierarchical issues but I tended to just go my own sweet way. I had always been a bit of a rebel in a quiet way and very strong-willed and nothing was going to change my personality. I wasn't prepared for that ever to happen. Things continued for the next few months and I was really happy. It was December and everyone was excited for Christmas.

It was my first Christmas as a real nurse. Sister Shutt said would I like to go shopping with her to get all the patients' and doctors' presents as she needed a hand. *Great*, I thought so we arranged to meet at the ward and she would drive us to the town.

I arrived in casual clothes and she appeared looking like a model as she had the face and figure to be one. Off we went to Debenhams, Boots and Marks and Spencer's. We were laden down with bags, ties for the consultants, socks for the juniors, soap sets, etc., for all and sundry. It was strange as I wasn't allowed to call her Stella still sister even though we were off duty.

She said, 'Would you like coffee?'

'Yes, that would be nice,' I replied, thinking we would go to a café. We pulled up outside of her flat, which was on the 3rd floor of a beautiful Georgian house. We struggled up the stairs with our purchases and inside we went. I sat on the large sofa and looked around it was a stunning room, very neat with expensive items and furniture.

She came into the room with a tray of porcelain cups and a matching plate with chocolate biscuits on and put it on the table in front of me. She sat down next to me and we started to talk initially about general stuff and then got to the more personal questions which was making me feel slightly uncomfortable and the fact that we were sat so close together.

Sister Shutt was talking and patting my leg. It made me on edge as this was my space. I had always felt myself freeze if anyone touched me or invaded my personal space I didn't really know, so this made me stiffen and feel very uncomfortable. We talked generally about everything current and then she started to talk about my eyes, saying how incredibly blue they were and so clear and open. She touched my hair, which was very blonde and long past my waist, saying how beautiful it was and how she wished hers was as lovely.

Her hand came up to my face where she said my skin was so clear and fresh. She leaned forward to kiss me. I froze and her mouth came onto mine and I jumped up saying what was she doing. I wasn't into girls. I was married and happy. She laughed at me trying to grab my hand to pull me forward towards her. I was pulling away and she was getting angry saying, she wanted it to be different as she thought I liked her and we could do this and no one needed to find out and she would ensure I got on and became more senior in my role.

I ran to the door not having a clue where I was. I bolted out into the street, looking around and saw a phone box and went to call my friend to come and get me. I daren't call Will or my family. I don't know what they would say or do to that matter.

I started to question myself. What did I do to encourage her to do this? Why do these things happen to me? I had never given any signs that I wanted this I was beyond bewildered. My friend arrived and I was pacing up and down, frantically looking around in case she came out after me. My friend was the only person I told and she also was in disbelief.

That night, I had to consider how I would handle seeing her. I decided I had to move jobs. I could not risk anything happening again in the future.

I went into the ward the next day for a late shift we were on together with 5 other staff. She didn't speak to me once. She went out of her way to work away from me. As the days went on, she was trying to pick me up on everything but not directly. It always went through someone else.

I felt that I was being singled out to do all the awful jobs, clean the sluice, change all the flowers, get the sputum specimens of which there were dozens of pots of gunk to collect. No one wanted that job, least of all me. She was punishing me as much as she could. That's it I am off looking for another job.

My application for further training to become a State Registered Nurse, was posted on my way to the supermarket; it was a shortened training of 2 years as already State Enrolled. I carried on trying to get by until May of the following year when my invite to interview came. I looked at it and was feeling myself well up, fearful I might not do well but I was made of strong stuff and my determination always takes me through.

The interview day arrived. I planned everything like a military exercise. I looked very professional and arrived at the school of nursing of a big teaching hospital and I was so excited I can't even begin to tell you. I sat in a large room with dozens of young women and a few young men. Not many were giving eye contact or speaking so I scanned the room for someone I thought looked receptive.

I had eye contact with a small blonde girl who smiled at me. She was the one I wanted to talk to. I went over and introduced myself. We hit it off immediately and it turned out we even went to the same secondary school. It was a long time before Karen was called in and when she came out said they were nice, a bit severe but would let her know.

I eventually went in and the panel was kind, smiling and asking questions about me and my family. They were keen to understand how I was going to manage a young child and study. I reassured them that my support network was incredible and Rebecca would never have other than her own family looking after her when I was working or studying. I seemed to be in with them for what seemed like hours but it obviously wasn't. 'We will be in touch,' I was told. I didn't know what to think. I did feel quite down.

I returned to my normal job on surgery; nothing changed, I still felt as though I was picked on. There seemed to be an atmosphere with another new member of staff. I felt I needed to know what was happening and why she felt the need to be off with me.

Jennifer was a naïve girl who recently qualified but wanted desperately to get on. We were on a late shift together and it was visiting time so most of us were in the ward office. I was in charge of the ward. I asked her directly if there was something I had done to upset her. She looked back angrily at me, stating that I should be ashamed of myself for trying to hit on the ward sister.

She had told her as they were together now and Stella didn't want her to think there was anything going on! What I said angrily how dare she. I then went about explaining how it happened and Jennifer's face became quite ashen. This is how we got together after a shopping trip for the ward.

At that point, I knew I was in serious trouble for my future. I wrote my notice then and there. I had to leave before my life became unbearable. How was I going to tell Will?

I got home that night after my shift. It was 10:30 PM, feeling sick with worry. Will met me at the door holding something and looking serious. I thought it was something dreadful. Before I could speak, he said go on open it. I stared at the envelope, not thinking what it could be. I ripped open the envelope and all I saw was *start 16th July.*

My head was all over the place. I read it properly and it was a place training for my State Registration. All I had wanted I had done it! It was 3 weeks away. I quickly did some calculations; I was owed 2 weeks holiday so it could easily be done.

I sat on the stairs and sobbed. Will was saying, 'What is wrong, don't you want it?' I then told him what had been going on. He was horrified. I had carried this on my own; he was so angry and wanted to go to speak to Stella.

34

I had said, 'No, leave it; he was reluctant but would respect my wishes.'

I went to work 2 days later after my days off and was on with Stella. I was mortified to see this. She was hostile to me and asked to see me in her office. I was really anxious as not a confrontational person. She closed the door and launched at me saying I was trying to ruin her reputation, was disrespectful to the consultants and I wasn't what she thought I was when she employed me.

I asked her if the consultant had complained about me; she stumbled over her words; I stopped her quickly saying, 'Mr Winton, kindly gave me a glowing reference for my new job. Also are there any complaints or concerns about my knowledge or nursing care?'

'No, there wasn't.' I had my hand on the door handle and said.

'Please, don't insult me. I didn't respond to your advances. I am not a shallow person. I have morals and I am a good nurse. I will be leaving in 2 weeks as I am taking my holiday.' I left shaking again, not knowing where that had come from.

The next 2 weeks went smoothly. Stella was off sick with a mystery illness. I was relieved. No one asked me any questions and the atmosphere was in all sense of the word "normal" but I felt uneasy; however, I was saddened to leave a speciality that I loved but was so excited about my future. Little did I know that this speciality would become my passion and my future.

Chapter Two

July 1980 arrived and I was so excited about my new training. I arrived at the school of nursing at the large teaching hospital, a new 2-storey building which still had a new smell but felt cold as so many bricks. I checked into the reception and was told to go to the main hall where I would be taken to my group.

I sat thinking what things were going to be like but so many things were going through my mind. The door opened and a large bosomed woman with a big smile came over to me. 'Hello, Maria. I am Mrs Southway's senior tutor. Let's have a chat.'

We went to her office and she outlined what would happen that day and a brief description of my course. She handed me some paperwork to sign and a folder with my name on which contained lots of papers.

We went to get measured up for my uniform, which resembled a kitchen J Cloth, blue check and nylon. I had a paper cap with 2 red stripes and was told I can get more caps when I need them. I was given a red long cape which was thick and warm as well as a diabolical navy flasher Mac and a little basin-type hat and told that I am not allowed out without it on at any cost.

I was given a whistle-stop tour of the hospital and then taken to my group, which was called a "set". We went into the large tutorial room and I was introduced to the group. There were 35 in the group and I was the only one joining after they had all done their first year of basic training. A lot of friendly faces smiled back at me and one girl named Tina beckoned to me to sit near her.

I settled into the group really quickly and realised who the characters were within no time. There was one particular girl who seemed to attract followers with her electric personality. She was life and soul and very beautiful, someone you wanted to be friends with. We had an amazing tutor, Tommy Thomas. He was the best and really cared about each and every one of us.

I immediately loved this group and became friends with 2 girls who lived in my village. I was able to offer them lifts home when they needed them.

We became a really tight group of friends and the whole group was a total delight. We did have the "know it all" Samuel, who seemed to have seen everything done everything and whatever you said, his experience was more dramatic than yours. He was a bit of a pain but he was our pain and we all protected him when others put him down.

My first ward was a gynaecology ward of 30 beds where various women's issues were dealt with. I was always conscious that women who were having infertility issues and those who were having early miscarriages were side by side with those who were in to have terminations and there appeared to be a great deal of those around this time. It wasn't uncommon for women to have terminations quite late on in pregnancy, which was so upsetting for the staff.

One particular day I was assigned six women who were having chemical (drug-induced) terminations of their pregnancies. I had to monitor their medication going through intravenously and assess their contractions and blood loss if they were bleeding.

The first termination I witnessed was of a woman in her late 40s who had been told the foetus was abnormal. She had gone through a lot of pain during her labour and wanted to push. I went behind the curtains to be with her and hold her hand. I sat her on a bedpan and she delivered a complete tiny body into it. It looked perfect at this point. We were both holding each other and sobbing. It was a moment I have never forgotten.

Many others were delivered here and some days you would go into the sluice and there would be bedpans lined up with little lifeless bodies in them with the mother's surname on the top before they went off to where ever they were sent to be examined.

On some occasions, the little bodies within the pans moved slightly. This was so distressing as there was absolutely nothing you could do. Thankfully, this didn't happen often. The ward sister on this ward was extremely hardened to this and showed no empathy towards the mother, which I found difficult to deal with. Thankfully, things have changed to prevent these events from reoccurring, which is a positive change.

It was whilst I was on this ward; I had a phone call to say my beloved grandfather passed away that morning. We were so close. I was devastated; the sister said you best go home then. No compassion, no concern if I would be all right to get home or anything. This I found hard to cope with as having compassion for your colleagues as well as your patients should come naturally as a nurse.

My next placement was trauma and orthopaedics, which consisted mostly of motorbike accidents, falls etc. It was a male ward and the average age was around 45.

This ward sister was a really strange woman who you didn't quite know if she liked you or she didn't. She tried not to communicate with you if she could help it. She was the partner of the sister on the medical ward below us who appeared to spend more time on our ward than her own! You felt you couldn't go to the office to ask a question as you were interrupting things and you got a really stern look.

I was assigned to look after Nigel, who was in a 25-year-old motorbike accident with 2 broken arms and 2 broken legs as well as a fractured jaw. How do I take his blood pressure as I couldn't get a cuff anywhere to do it?

Sister Van Herp suggested I use his neck! She laughed and said work it out and closed the door on me. I didn't know what I was supposed to do. I was, after all, a student so needed guidance which I never got from this woman. I didn't really like this speciality so was glad when that was over.

Unfortunately, I then went to another area, which wasn't for me at all—psychiatry. The pace of this work was really slow and I found the staff to be an even bigger issue. They appeared too laid back, were much happier sitting in the office all chatting together and on this particular unit, which was acute, there was a constant smell of drugs even in the staff office.

I hated this placement beyond words. The only bit of advice I was given on starting this placement from the charge nurse was don't take any Maltesers from Joan and then he laughed. I had no idea what he was saying and I wouldn't take sweets anyway from a patient. I later found out that Joan used to roll up her faeces into little balls and offer them as Maltesers in a box!

To this day, it's put me off these little chocolates. I found one of the patients extremely disturbing. He seemed to always be high on drugs and was violent, which made me nervous. The staff appeared to find it amusing and just let him get on with it. He was having a sexual relationship with one of the female patients with anorexia and you would frequently walk in on them having sex just wherever the fancy took them and even when you walked in they didn't stop; it was very unnerving.

When he wasn't having sex with the other patient, he could just walk into an area and masturbate anywhere even if there were visitors present. No one ever question or tried to discourage these actions. I was so very uncomfortable in this environment. This unit wasn't attached to my training hospital and we were sent there for three months which was tortuous for me as I was so frustrated as to how these poor patients were being treated or not treated more to the point.

I spoke with my tutor Tommy and he was sympathetic, saying I wasn't the first to have mentioned this and that we would all be pulled out of this unit in the next year. Sadly, I had to do my "time" but my set was the last one that had to endure this awful environment. To my knowledge, it was under investigation soon after and the staff were suspended, the seniors all being demoted.

Next was the general medical ward where there was a good variety of conditions for me to learn about and I found this a really great place to work. The sister again was a tyrant but a real nurse who was there for her patients. She led by example and that I admired. I was working on this ward with one of my set and that was great. We did nights together, also which wasn't so great as I never enjoyed nights.

Sister Ford liked us as we worked hard and she was a great teacher. Medical students used to come onto the ward and she would usher them off, saying patients need to rest and they needed to clear it with her before upsetting her ward. I learnt so much from her and am grateful as some of my experiences came in handy in later life.

There was, however, a staff nurse who plastered herself in makeup and perfume but had the worst body odour you could ever imagine. We didn't think she washed her uniforms as the underarms were like cardboard. She obviously wasn't aware of the fact the smell was horrendous. The rest of the team suggested we drew straws as to who was going to tell her. Yes, you guessed it: I got the short one!

I waited until we were on together and started talking about washing powders etc. It turned out she didn't wash her dresses and wore the same one for 2 weeks as she didn't have a washing machine. I couldn't bring myself to come out with it but used the "someone I had worked with before" scenario whose clothes were holding odour.

It worked. She didn't smell after this. She managed to get new uniforms and was regularly laundering them through the hospital laundry service so that was a job well done without hurting her feelings!

We had the best time as student nurses we worked hard and laughed harder the system as it was at this time was so different from what we see today. Our training was mostly hands-on and had blocks of theory to back it up.

We were nurses from the outset got stuck in and weren't wrapped in cotton wool. We saw it as it really was but we had the protection of our tutors and the support from each other it was the best time ever. Our cupboards with full to the brim with stock, our resources were available to us with no bureaucratic red tape and reels of paperwork to complete.

We could get a district nurse to go and see our patients when they were discharged. We knew the patients would get so much support and get everything that was needed to get them back to their normal self. We had rehabilitation and convalescent homes to get patients back to top form. Where did it all go so wrong?

Managers were few and far between in my student days. The ward sister was the person who must be obeyed, obviously the charge nurse (male equivalent) too. We had the nursing officer who was above the sister/charge nurse. They would oversee several wards, usually within a speciality and there were only a few of these in a hospital. You will see how this changed as you read on.

I was now in my final year of training and seen as a "senior". I now had three red stripes on my cap and this came with a given respect from the junior students – one I or any of my set didn't take advantage of we just enjoyed the journey.

I was allocated to a general surgical ward, which was an area I enjoyed so very much. I was there with one of my good friends and we were frequently working together, which was great. We came on for a late shift, which was nine hours and got into the normal routine

One of the patients hadn't been well for some days and sadly passed away. We were asked to perform "last offices" on him, which we started to prepare for. Kelly looked at me nervously and said she had never done this before and was really fearful. I advised her we would do this together and she would be fine.

We went behind the curtains and started to wash John. I was talking to him the whole time saying what we were doing. Kelly looked at me slightly puzzled. I continued. As I said we were to wash his back and I would roll him to me, the movement caused John to expel air from his lungs causing what sounded like a huge sigh.

Kelly squealed and ran off. I went to find her explaining what had just happened. She was visibly quivering but came back in. We carried on and then Kelly went to wash John's bottom. He passed a large amount of wind at this point and Kelly started to go a strange shade of grey and was about to vomit.

I grabbed the washing bowl with flannel and soap sat in the water and held it under her chin. She vomited for what seemed like an age. I sent her to sit down and I finished things on my own. It was a traumatic experience for her but thankfully John was given every respect. It was another one of those events that will stay with me forever.

My final placements were really enjoyable; initially I worked in the community with a fantastic district nursing sister named Michelle. She was brilliant, kind, caring and so hardworking. Her husband and I were going to meet on a future placement. I enjoyed working within this setting except for one exception of driving home along a dual carriageway, after a shift visiting families at home, it was the height of summer and I saw what looked like the freckles on my arms moving. No, it wasn't freckles but I was covered in fleas!

I found myself driving at a ridiculously fast speed. Why? I'm not sure as I didn't know what I would do when I got home! I had to get hosed down in the garden, strip off and then run to the shower. My car had to be fumigated. Funny now but not at the time.

I met Michelle's husband on my final placement in coronary care. He was a senior registrar and a delightful man who always had time for everyone and didn't make you feel stupid. He taught us so much and the unit was exceptional with such high standards of care. There were stressful moments but they were handled so professionally and calmly making you feel as though you were being guided through the trauma and potential mayhem, preparing you for any eventualities in the future.

I gained skills, which were priceless, on this placement and felt part of the team even as a student. The area was so well-controlled in an emergency situation and it gave an unspoken confidence to all who worked there.

My final examination day arrived and we all met for breakfast and there was a nervousness in the air as we all chattered pretending not to be anxious. We were ushered to our seats and papers were upside down on the desk. First was multiple choice and then the main paper 3 hours later we were finished.

Well, we couldn't do any more so we all left and digested each other's answers. Each of us feeling we might have got some wrong. We could choose where we could work whilst waiting for our results. I decided to work in the emergency department, which was busy and always unexpected. The work was enjoyable, again getting new skills.

Trauma cases came in thick and fast motorcycle, car, cycle and even the occasional tractor and crane injury – all needed close attention and support. One of the worse things I remember was a young man who was cycling to work one morning and a works van came around the corner on the wrong side of the road and almost decapitated him. I have never seen so much blood in all my days.

He arrived with us barely alive. It was horrendous. He also sustained multiple other injuries and these were too much for his body to endure. He sadly lost his life in our resuscitation room – a day I will always remember – one I would prefer not to have to remember. His life snuffed out in an instant. He was 22 years of age; seeing the look on his mother's face chilled me to the bone. All because someone had been out the night before and was late getting up for work. Tragic in every sense of the word.

The day arrived for results; we all met at the school of nursing, very anxious. Our letters were handed to us, screeches of delight were heard all around the room. I had passed. I was now a fully qualified registered nurse. Sadly, one of our group and my good friend Kelly was the only one who didn't pass. She made the decision that day she would not retake the exam despite us all giving her encouragement to do so.

To this day, she didn't retake it but went down the route of nursing auxiliary and was a successful school nurse. She was a really good nurse and is still a good friend. My family was delighted and my parents bought me a beautiful and precious antique silver buckle to wear with my uniform, which I will always treasure.

Chapter Three

Now I had to think about where I wanted to work. The job market at this time was competitive, as so many people wanted jobs. I decided I didn't want to work where I had trained not because it wasn't a great place to work but because I felt I needed to get out of my comfort zone and learn new things.

Each hospital did things differently and the paperwork etc., varied from place to place. Where I was, there were around a dozen good places to work, easily commutable, so I set out looking for a job. I applied for several but wanted to work in a surgery setting. I had three interview offers, so thought I would see which one felt right, should I be offered any positions.

I attended all interviews, smartly presented and they were quite formal but I managed not to make a complete fool of myself. One of the panels at one of the interviews (there were four people on each one!) was a bit of a comedian and wanted to make a joke out of everything that was said, which was rather off-putting. I wasn't quite sure what to make of it.

I was offered two out of the three jobs but decided on the one which was closest to my home, as we did have good underground links on both ends. I accepted the job and had a start date of four weeks, which was perfect.

The day quickly came and there I was, standing in my staff nurse blue-striped dress, frilly cap and white starched apron. My solid silver buckle, which was antique and beautiful, was displayed with pride on my blue petersham belt. I felt so proud.

I started my induction period and was allocated to the senior staff nurse, Joanna. She was a tall and slim girl with sad, large brown eyes that seemed to stare at you. She was efficient and not one for any small talk; she was what seemed to be a bit of a loner and always sat on her own in breaks and was found reading at every opportunity she wasn't working on the ward. No one really knew her, it seemed.

The ward was busy with several specialities and theatre lists constantly, no real let up, with the ward having forty beds, which was a large number of patients. We did, however, have a large workforce of nurses, so we were never short of staff or struggling to get the work done.

Joanne was difficult to talk to and didn't really give any feedback on how I was doing. I wanted to approach her but could never find the right time to do so.

One Sunday morning after I had been working on the ward for around three months, she didn't arrive for her shift. I was working with her and it was out of character she hadn't called in to say she was sick and hadn't spoken with anyone. I rang the nursing officer to say we were a person down on the ward. I was the only registered nurse on duty with a team of enrolled and nursing auxiliaries.

A couple of hours later, the nursing officer arrived with a policeman; they both looked anxious. I was taken into the office and asked some questions about when I last saw her, what was she like and others which were strange in nature. I asked why I was being asked this.

They looked at each other and the policeman nodded at my nursing officer. She put her hand on my arm and said something awful had happened to Joanna but they couldn't give the full details. The rest of the shift was a bit of a blur, none of the staff could totally concentrate but we got through it.

A few days later, we were all told that it seemed Joanna had driven her car off a cliff; no one knew she was depressed or suffering in any way, as those who knew her said she had always been a loner and behaved this way.

Life was different after this. We were so bewildered and angry. We hadn't recognised she was suffering. It certainly made us all aware of others around us, no matter how busy we were.

More details emerged as the weeks went on. It appeared that she had been having a relationship with one of the managers in another city hospital where she had previously worked. His wife was also a manager in this hospital and found out about the affair.

Joanna moved jobs but continued on the relationship. The manager said he was going to leave his wife for her. The wife then applied for a job at the hospital where Joanna then worked and started to threaten her saying she would expose her sordid life and the fact that she was breaking up a family.

Joanna couldn't cope with this but never spoke a word to anyone about what this woman was putting her through. It seemed there were a lot more awful things but we didn't get to know about them. There were some dreadful things said and done which eventually tipped Joanna over the edge.

She left a note in her flat saying what had happened and she was sorry. Her only downfall was she fell in love with someone who was never going to leave his wife and lied to her. We were all shaken by what we heard and the things that were revealed. Poor girl, if only she would have spoken to one of us.

I became unsettled after twelve months on this ward and felt I needed to move on to something new. My own personal life was fine, although I did feel I was changing as a person, almost feeling the need to experience other things. I seemed to be growing in a different direction.

I applied for midwifery training. In those days it was a natural progression to do general and then midwifery or paediatric nursing so the eighteen-month training sounded just what I needed. I applied to an excellent women's hospital and was accepted with a start date of 3 months. I gave my notice and started to get a little excited, as I loved new challenges.

I arrived and my group had 12 student midwives in it. I knew one already as we were in the same set for our general nursing; she was never someone I gelled with naturally but I made an effort and it was fine on a professional level. There were two other students who were married and we seemed to click and enjoyed each other's company.

We started our placements and I worked in the ante-natal ward first, which I really enjoyed. There was such a mix of mums-to-be first timers, old timers etc. I enjoyed the variety of experiences of these women and the stories they had about previous labours, etc.

The first-time mum's eyes were wide when the more experienced mums gave blow-by-blow accounts of their dreadful labours and delivery. It seemed to be a bit of a competition at times who had the worst time. Most of the women there had some complications in pregnancy, that's why they had to stay in.

One young woman Caroline was having twins. She had been in the hospital on bed rest since she was 18 weeks pregnant; she was now thirty-two weeks pregnant (pregnancy normally lasts forty weeks) and had to stay until delivery due to her unstable blood pressure and diabetes. She was twenty-two years old and so down she had a two-year-old at home and a husband who she was constantly concerned about. He didn't cope very well at the best of times.

One particular day, I was doing some general tidying of the ward when the emergency buzzer was screaming out. I was literally just across the hall from the room it was coming from. It was Caroline's room. I ran in to find her on the floor having what looked like a grand mal seizure, laying in a pool of blood.

Another student midwife was there. She pressed the emergency call bell. She was frozen to the spot. I went into emergency mode getting her onto her side in the recovery position. I ensured she was not going to harm herself. I looked to see where the bleeding was coming from. It was, it seemed, from the genital area and was continuing to come.

I shouted to call the crash team (the emergency team who deal with major events such as cardiac arrest) and someone dialled the infamous number 888; this went through to the red phone in the switchboard to alert them it was an emergency. The team arrived, Caroline had stopped breathing and resuscitation had been commenced. It was the first priority to save her and then her babies.

We worked on her for over an hour but she could not be revived so pronounced dead. It was surreal…it wasn't happening in real time…everything had slowed down and it didn't feel that we were even there. The next thing was to check as fast as possible on the babies. As soon as her clothing was lifted, it was apparent that she had spontaneously aborted her babies and had had a huge haemorrhage.

The placenta had sheered away from the uterine wall causing a massive bleed (placenta abruption). This starves the babies of oxygen and consequently they die. Caroline had some contraction pains but was told it was most likely Braxton Hicks contractions, which are false labour pains that many women feel in the second or third trimester of pregnancy and are deemed normal.

There was no indication to think otherwise. The excessive bleeding sent her into shock and caused the seizure. The situation was just dreadful. Everyone on duty was in total shock and the tears flowed freely. How do you deal with something like this and not feel distraught?

The poor husband was inconsolable. He sobbed into the arms of the consultant who also cried openly; there was an air of doom and disbelief over the whole ward. Those on duty were given three days off to have some time to reflect and come to terms with the events. It's not something you can do easily.

We had to move on but it wasn't easy.

Post-natal was next and I loved the babies but the mothers in many cases felt they were ill and wanted to be waited upon. This wasn't the case for everyone, of course, but the minority.

Some had to be constantly reminded they have had a baby, not a limb removed so could get up out of bed.

Some of the mothers had gone through a lot in their labour and delivery without question and these mums were given extra care and attention. Some had psychological issues after a traumatic labour. This was dealt with sympathetically too.

What I didn't like was that the mums who had stillborn babies or had spontaneous abortions (miscarriages) were nursed in the same ward as those who had healthy babies. It seemed cruel and unnecessary for these women and their partners suffered unspeakable heartache. It was voiced several times to managers but we were told 'That was how it's always been!' So change it, we said, 'This fell on deaf ears and never got changed in this department in my time there but would be confident that things are different now.'

I was then moved to the labour ward, another area I really enjoyed. That one-to-one with a couple and giving them your undivided attention was so satisfying. There was a terrifying senior midwife that looked like the grim reaper with long bony fingers. You didn't want to be on duty with her as she was a little creepy. Couldn't put my finger on why she was but she was.

As a student you had to have your examinations checked to make sure you were right, that was fine but on talking to all my colleagues, we could never understand why was it that after her vaginal examinations of the patients, their waters seemed to break!

It was very strange. To say the least until one day we witnessed why. She was right-handed and the index finger of her right hand had the longest most pointed nail I had ever seen. When she put her finger in the glove, it popped through the end and when inserted into the vagina up to the cervix, pop it went through the membranes!

She was furious when one of my colleagues questioned her why it happened. Her answer was if we don't rupture these women's membranes, we will all be here all day and night! She retired not long after we left the labour wards but I did wonder how many she had actually done this to and if there were any infections or injuries as it was like a dagger.

We hated night duty and myself and my two married friends cried when we had to do nights where we hated them so much. None of us could sleep during the day and the witching hours between three and five were the worst.

One night had been really busy, everyone was in with women in labour. I had just finished my delivery and completed my paperwork. I thought might as well have my break and I opened my lunch box to see salmon and cucumber sandwiches staring up at me. *Great*, I thought as I enjoyed the first one. Suddenly the outside buzzer rang, usually a woman in labour in the middle of the night.

I jumped up to see a man leaping up and down at the door screaming quick, be quick. Sandwich still in hand I ran out to him. 'It's the wife she wants to push.' I looked in the back of the van and a large lady was sprawled across some tyres screaming, 'I'm gonna push this little sod out anytime now.' I looked at my sandwich and thought, *Oh, no. I'm not wasting this,* so shoved it all in my mouth, grabbed my gloves from my pocket and tried to deliver her baby whilst wrestling with her tights and a mouthful of salmon so couldn't speak!

I could see the head, so through the Hovis, I am saying, 'pant pant.' I delivered a large nine-and-a-half-pound baby girl, practically with the tights still on. I found out it was her sixth child. Luckily, everyone was fine and I really enjoyed my salmon sandwich and not a crumb was lost.

Many babies were born in this unit and some were so memorable happy and sad experiences we had. I delivered a baby of a young girl, aged just twelve. She wouldn't tell anyone who the father was and concealed the pregnancy for the whole nine months until she had abdominal pains and was taken to the hospital to be examined.

She was found to be in the early stages of labour and transferred to the delivery suite. I welcomed her with her mother and uncle. She was a small girl who looked like a child and behaved as a child but was about to become a mother. I chatted to her and she responded to me well. We seemed to hit it off. I explained everything to her and said I needed to examine her internally and listen to her baby's heart. She didn't react like someone who was about to give birth and carried on reading her comic, just saying 'OK.'

I gained permission to examine her and found she was in established labour and was in fact six centimetres dilated (0-10 is the scale with 10 being fully dilated and ready to push). Her mother just sat not saying a word neither did the uncle. Who I did ask to leave the room when I examined her; Mum stayed the whole time at my request. Stacey was her name and she didn't seem to want to speak with her mum and I got the impression there wasn't the best of relationships going on here.

I stepped out to discuss my findings and the case with the senior midwife on duty. She listened intently and said, 'Well, it's your case. Call me if you get into any difficulty; you seem to have it covered.' She gave a flippant comment about Stacey, saying how these young girls ask for trouble these days. I stood open-mouthed as she walked away; we didn't know how this had happened or any of the circumstances. It wasn't our place to be judgmental. It was our place to care for and protect Stacey and her baby whilst in our charge.

I went back to the room and found her mum huddled in a corner with the uncle whispering Stacey was still looking at her comic. Mum said they were going for a coffee and didn't give Stacey a second glance, just left. I pulled up a chair and sat with her.

She looked at me with tears in her eyes as she had another contraction and grabbed for my hand. I held her hand and spoke softly to her, encouraging her to breathe through the pain. We had discussed pain relief and she said she was fine and didn't want it. Stacey started to speak to me and seemed to want to tell me things, almost as a way of relieving the pressure she had been under.

It was soon established that the baby was conceived from abuse that she had suffered but she wouldn't say from who; it was obvious that it was a family member by the things she told me. Stacey had never had a boyfriend. We talked about all sorts of things. I made her laugh and she became more relaxed as time went on, well in between the contractions, anyway.

I promised to stay with her and deliver her baby; she didn't want anyone else and each time another midwife came into the room, she would become stiff and not speak, so I decided to stay on. I informed the midwife in charge, who told me I was stupid to do this for her as she wouldn't appreciate it, nor would it be remembered. She was very bitter when she was speaking about her and that shocked me somewhat, as there was no compassion for this child.

Thankfully, nature is often kind to young girls in labour and it didn't last too long around eight hours. It was time to push. The uncle wanted to watch and I felt that it wasn't appropriate as Stacey became very upset at this request, so I asked him to leave. He was abusive to me and said it was "his right" to stay. I rang the emergency bell to get help to have him removed.

Security was quickly on the scene and took him out. At that point the mother was screaming at me, so again I had to get help. Stacey was so distraught and sobbing whilst trying to push out her baby. It was at this point she cried out that her uncle was the father of the baby. I was in total disbelief and the other two midwives who came to help me were ashen and shocked and almost rooted to the spot.

The mother started to launch at Stacey and hit me in the process. I was scrubbed up to deliver the baby and tried to fend her off. The situation was so unreal and, with that, a barrage of people ran into the room pulling the mother out. I was bleeding on my cheek and managed to just control the baby being born despite my shaking and crying.

I would never want to relive this again. I had to sit down as soon as the baby was out my legs were like jelly, I couldn't stand. Stacey was silent and white. She was so scared but she was fine and so was the beautiful little baby girl she had just brought into the world in the strangest of settings. Stacey held out her arms to me and wanted comfort. I held her close telling her it would be all right and for her not to worry. She was safe.

The police had arrived at this point and were waiting to speak with me and Stacey; the senior midwife had called them as she had heard Stacey say about her uncle. Her attitude seemed to have changed after hearing this, she became compassionate and concerned for Stacey.

The situation was horrendous and didn't improve. Stacey and her baby were taken into foster care, her mum and uncle arrested. Stacey's mum was charged with assault of three healthcare professionals, me being one of them. I had never bargained for this to happen. We had to give statements about the situation. It was so surreal.

Stacey went with her baby into a young mother's unit where she was cared for. She then went into a family on long-term fostering where she stayed, I understand, until she was eighteen and moved out with Jodie her little girl. They were safe and healthy.

It was a sad situation and again something which took its toll on our mental well-being.

My community experience was the best as a student midwife I was so fortunate to work with an amazing midwife who was adored by so many. She had delivered so many babies in the area and had been in the community for over 20 years. Her sadness was she herself could never have children of her own due to a condition she had but she channelled her love through the babies she cared for. Her husband seemed so supportive and loving too.

Mary was a large jolly woman who had a broad Irish accent her love of the job oozed out of her. I was always running behind her it seemed and one particular day there was a cascade of popping sounds; she had a bad case of wind! She kept walking, not saying a word and I was frantically looking around in case someone thought I was doing this. I noticed it happened daily after this so I then thought I think I will try to walk in front of Mary. It didn't change anything.

We had our daily calls to perform and Mary gave me some to do on my own, which I got on with. I attended a lovely lady due to home birth for her second child. I hadn't met her before but was advised she liked everything holistic and natural. She was having a Leboyer method of delivery. This is where the room is dimly lit, very quiet and the baby is placed directly on the mother's skin to avoid any unnecessary stress to the newly born child (Frederick Leboyer a French physician 1919–2017).

Lilly was a quietly spoken articulate woman with a soft Scottish lilt to her voice, very soothing; it made you speak quietly back. She was on the floor, when I arrived on bean bags, naked and also her husband and three-year-old daughter were there too. The room was dark and warm. Lily was in established labour her waters had broken and she was very calm.

I attempted to contact Mary but couldn't get hold of her over the radio. I was starting to get worried as I hadn't ever delivered a baby out of the hospital. I was nervous and kept trying to get hold of Mary. In the end, I left a message at the health centre telling them to get hold of her urgently, I needed her here.

Lily whispered it was time to push her baby out, as she said this her husband looked at me and said please let it be better than her last experience. We don't want her in that state again. I was reeling from this statement as I didn't know what he meant.

Lily silently pushed her little boy into the world and I placed him onto her bare skin. He was alert and breathing well with no adverse issues. I was a little shaky but not so you would notice. The room remained silent the baby gave a little cry but was so calm. A loud bashing on the door jolted us all it was Mary larger than life. She came rushing in mumbling, 'Thank you, lord, thank you.' She patted me on the head, saying, Well done, girl. I was so bewildered by the whole situation. I was thinking, well, that was so easy. What was the fuss about?'

After clearing up and making sure mum and baby were well and safe, Mary and I went off to have a cup of tea back at the health centre. We sat down and Mary was looking at me long and hard. 'I'm sorry I wasn't there for you,' she said, 'but trying to sort out my husband. He has left me for one of the receptionists at the clinic. He wants a child and I can't give that to him so he's gone.'

My mouth fell open and I started to say, 'I am so..." Mary put her hand up in front of me and said no more to be said on the matter, it's done. I didn't argue. She started to discuss the delivery and the possible danger the mother was in and that of her child.

We didn't have the previous notes, as her baby was born on the Isle of Skye in a remote place. She was extremely ill in labour and had to be airlifted by the obstetric flying squad to a major unit in Glasgow as she developed a uterine inversion (a rare complication where the uterus/womb turns either partially or completely inside out. The woman goes into shock and can bleed heavily, which can result in death).

As Mary was explaining this to me, I could feel the colour draining away and my head was full of what could have happened. We were not aware of the previous events until that day as apparently we were waiting for her notes and they were held up for whatever reason. Lily should have had a consultant-led delivery but went into labour a bit earlier than expected so nothing was in place. Should I not have gone there that day, she would have delivered on her own.

I was shaken but Mary supported me throughout despite her own personal grief. She was, without question, one of the best people I had ever worked with and there had been a few. My final report was glowing and emphasised my work in a crisis and dealing with adverse events safely and confidently. I was very pleased with this.

Being in the community had various challenges and some were scary, I won't lie. I attended a post-natal check on a young mum on the eighteenth floor of a high-rise building. It was worrying and a place I felt very uneasy. Graffiti was everywhere, people shouting and screaming and the smell of stale urine in the lift didn't help. I arrived at the flat to be met by a very skinny young man in his pants, he beckoned me in.

The young mum was sitting on the sofa, pale and dishevelled. There were numerous other young men milling around the room and a lot of activity going on. The room was very smoky with several dogs jumping around and barking at me. I'm not afraid of dogs but kept my hands high just in case. I looked down to see the tiny three-day-old baby laying on the floor with a bottle propped up by cushions in its mouth.

I was gravely concerned. The skinny lad asked me if I wanted a cup of tea. I declined politely, saying I had just had one. Nevertheless, he thrust a pint mug with Guinness written on the side into my hand. It had obviously come from the local pub and I noticed everyone had a glass, no cups or mugs in here it seemed. I didn't want to appear rude so popped the mug onto the floor (as this seemed to be the place they all used) by the side of my seat whilst I attended to mum and baby.

It was extremely distracting as it transpired that someone had just stolen a television from somewhere else and these lads were trying to install it in the flat. It was a real education for me.

Mum was depressed. Her milk was coming in and she felt very down she was only sixteen and had no mother figure to help her. I spoke with her about the importance of keeping everything sterilised, not putting the baby on the floor, keeping the dogs away, etc.

I then spoke with the skinny lad who was the dad and advised him that smoking around his baby was dangerous; he was right on it opening the windows and telling his friends it wouldn't be allowed any more. Great, he heard what I was saying. Another result was putting my mug of tea on the floor, the dogs lapped it up—result!

I did make two further visits to this couple and Mary came with me just so we could be sure the family was safe. The GP was informed and the health visitor was to ensure ongoing support. The family, I believe, did well and listened to all the advice given I was relieved.

My finals were a two-part affair written and a viva where you were quizzed by some very experienced midwives and obstetricians; they gave you props and scenarios and if you didn't get it right, then you failed. I seem to have had the oldest midwife on the planet who didn't give eye contact or engage in any talk other than the question.

The obstetrician was lovely like an uncle who wanted you to do well. His questions were straightforward and I answered them fully. I then had a model of a pelvis and a ragged old doll of a baby. I was asked abruptly to show how I would deliver a breach presentation (usually feet first).

I went through the things I would check and proceeded to say how to deliver. She was visibly angry and told me to get on with it. The consultant was himself angry with her for being so rude and told her so. So, in the middle of my viva examination, my two examiners were arguing with each other and the whole of the room stopped to look over, it took four others to stop them from almost coming to blows! Another situation which I hadn't bargained for.

I passed my midwifery exams and worked in midwifery for six months, deciding it wasn't for me. I decided it was time for me to go back to general nursing and up the ladder.

I applied for a post as a ward sister in a small care of an elderly hospital of four wards. This hospital was part of a much larger group of hospitals but had its own management team. I got the post and was so happy. The hospital was run by a senior nursing officer and a hospital secretary named Reginald who had slicked-back grey hair and always wore a pinstriped suit.

He looked like someone from an Agatha Christie play. He kept hold of the purse strings but we never wanted for a thing. He was quite intimidating until you got to know him. The senior nursing officer was officious and aloof and always smelled heavily of cigarette smoke, which I have always hated and couldn't help the look on my face when she was near to me. They spent a lot of time in their offices but the hospital was run like clockwork and so clean you could eat your dinner off of the floor.

We had a visiting GP who came once a week to see our patients and write prescriptions and sorted any issues. Dr Lofthouse was a nervous man who came in and ran around the ward, trying to get out as fast as possible. He had the sense of humour of a snail and was uncomfortable around females which was evident. He blushed when talking to us and was better if there were a few of us but not on a one-to-one basis.

The staff were a great bunch and most were a little older. They used to love our banter and my tales saying working with me was like a soap opera! I started a Bachelor's degree in healthcare whilst in this post, funding it myself with no study time granted and distance learning. I soon gained my BSc in Healthcare and honours with it. The post was a great starting block for gaining more experience but I was getting restless and needed a challenge.

Whilst I was looking for posts, Reginald was arrested for fraud. It was found by the finance officer of the larger hospital that ran our one that over fifty thousand pounds were unaccounted for over a ten-year period. The hospital was always in credit, clean, had no complaints, always had everything you needed, who would have guessed that Reginald was up to these things and for so long.

He ended up with a prison sentence and the senior nurse was suspended from her post but reinstated as was unaware of the situation.

Chapter Four

I then moved to a large teaching hospital where I became the sister of an acute medical ward. The ward had four consultants, three old school and a "jack the lad" more recent appointment. He was known for being someone who liked a good time drinking and one for the ladies, also a very heavy smoker who loved to plaster himself in a cologne, which was pungent and slightly nauseating, to say the least.

I made a friend with one of the staff nurses on an adjacent ward. She was a great person but seemed to sleep her way around anyone with a pulse. Janine always maintained she would marry a doctor and wouldn't settle for anyone else. She said she didn't need to love him as long as the status was there. She became the talk of everyone and it seemed that so many made it almost a game to see if she would sleep with them. They needn't have worried she would!

I remained friends with her for all of my career, although we never really socialised. I was having issues in my personal life and felt that my solid and stable marriage had hit the buffers and I was unsure of my future. Will was working hard and so was I, Rebecca was a happy child, but I didn't know what was happening to me. We were trying to do up our house, but I felt I like was living in a building site and constant mess, which I couldn't cope with it.

The ward was busy and always full so kept me on my toes; I was wrapped up in my work. I didn't notice my world tumbling around me. I was on duty and it was the beginning of August when the medical staff rotate and you have a new bunch of doctors to orientate to the environment. Dr Russell, our senior consultant, brought in the new doctors and I was immediately drawn to one who had the most amazing eyes and smile.

I found myself blushing which didn't happen often. Each one was introduced to me separately but I was only really looking at one. Dr Mark Cox was our new senior house officer and it certainly brightened my day. I found that I couldn't get him out of my thoughts and hoped he would come to the ward every time I heard the front doors open. I found that he was coming to the ward much more often than the others, which I was pleased about.

The weeks went on and we talked a lot and had coffee together people were noticing but we weren't doing anything wrong. I was not wanting to have my days off as I wouldn't see him. I was not my usual self at home I knew that. Janine had already made a play for him but he wasn't having any of it from her.

The house was a mess; Will was working on it for me to get it how I wanted it but it wasn't what I really wanted. I did some extra shifts, yes, we could do with the money but I wanted to be on the ward just to see Mark. What was happening to me? I was beginning to get scared.

I remember this as if it were yesterday. It was two in the afternoon and Mark came to ask me to help him perform a procedure on one of our patients she was profoundly deaf. I prepared the patient in the procedure room and in he came and gave me a huge smile. He was so gentle and held the patient's hand whilst trying to explain everything to her before starting. It wasn't too bad a procedure and would help her hearing, that was for sure.

He kept looking at me whilst getting everything ready and I had my hand on her shoulder and he put his on top of mine. I flushed so much and my legs were weak. I knew then that this was going much further than I thought and really quickly. He carried on the procedure, not saying anything personal to me in front of the patient, just in case but the touch of his hand on mine whenever possible and the look deep into my eyes made me melt.

I took the patient back to the ward and came back to clear up. He walked towards me as I came in and closed the door, reaching past me and getting so very close. He said he wanted to kiss me at this point. Nothing happened I am too professional for that, but it so nearly did.

Things got worse; I was moody at home, couldn't settle, and there was only one thing on my mind. There was a party at the hospital the next week and I planned to go. Will wouldn't have been happy for me to do this, as he was very possessive of me I was determined to go. I said I was doing a night shift so planned ahead.

I took my clothes to work after Will had left and put them in my locker. The evening had come and I preened myself and put on my uniform. My makeup was different and did get noticed, but I said I didn't realise. Off I went to "work".

I arrived at the ward and quickly changed into my party clothes and set off to see Mark feeling so nervous. I went to the doctors' mess where it was and saw him looking out of the window; he saw me and his face lit up and he came out to see me. Before going in, he pulled me to the side of the building in a dark area and kissed me. I was putty in his hands. I felt like I was me again and had an amazing evening. We then went back to his room and I stayed all night.

I was so confused and so guilty that I couldn't eat or sleep. I was losing so much weight; I felt sick all the time. The relationship continued and he declared he loved me and wanted me to leave my family. I was in total turmoil. I had lost two stones in weight and I couldn't concentrate. I went to see my doctor, who knew me well and suggested I got away for a few days to think.

Will thought it was the pressure of work generally and wanted to take me away but I didn't want to go with him so I said I would go with my older sister, just to get some girl time. He reluctantly agreed. I spoke with my sister and told her what was going on, she herself had had a similar thing happen so was sympathetic to my needs and said she would do whatever I needed.

I packed my bag and Will wanted to drive me to Brighton where we were going. I said, 'No, I needed to do this myself.' I went to collect Mark and we went off to a beautiful country hotel where we chatted and snuggled up for three days. I didn't want it to end. I was missing Rebecca but that was all. I didn't call home at all, as I wanted to clear my head.

We made our way home and I went to Mark's house. He said, 'Stay, don't go.' I knew it was wrong what I was doing but I was in love with two people and I had to choose. I looked around Mark's house and it was almost like a student's house, clothes and "things" everywhere. That wasn't for me. I like everything neat and tidy and clean. I was having doubts.

I went home and Will stood at the door with Rebecca and my heart was racing. I was crying as I looked at them they were so pleased to see me. I ran in and said I need to talk to you and a look of anguish came over his face. We sat down after putting Rebecca to bed and I told him that I had to get away as I had developed feelings for another man. He asked me if I loved him, I said, 'I think so but I love you too.'

He was crying and I wasn't prepared for that. He said did I want him to leave or me to leave again, I said no. Not once did he ask me if I had kissed or slept with him. That night Will took an overdose of paracetamol. It was one of the most horrendous times and I was racked with guilt. Will was admitted to the hospital but thankfully was fine, I spoke with the psychiatrist who came to see him (this was a normal occurrence when this happened).

He wasn't deemed to be at risk so we sat and talked it through for hours and hours. We decided to move away from the area and thought the south coast would be an option as his company had an outlet there and I could get a job easily. The ball was put in motion; the house went on the market.

I saw Mark a few times and still desperately wanted him but couldn't stand the thought of hurting so many or splitting my family. I felt it was a better outcome for just me to be upset than everyone. I saw my GP, who diagnosed depression and anxiety I was put on medication to help and reluctantly, I took them.

We moved houses and jobs and tried to pick up the pieces. We had a nice three bed semi near Eastbourne and I got a job as a ward sister in surgery, which was my passion. The ward was huge, forty-six beds mixed sex and had major surgical cases. I was interviewed for a different post initially but was given the choice.

The nursing officer was Mrs Butcher "Butch" as she was known as a real character who was as tall as she was wide. Everyone loved her but she was exasperating. I liked her immediately. I was introduced to my team on my induction and they all seemed great and welcoming. I didn't realise just how many issues these lovely people would give me.

My second-in-command senior staff nurse (SSN) was Jim. he was a very experienced nurse but socially awkward. He was married with a child and lived a stone's throw from the hospital. There were many characters on my team. Jill was a northern lass who was a tomboy and tried to outdo the males at every opportunity. She was trying too hard to get a boyfriend and any unsuspecting male that came on the ward she flirted with.

She had to be reined in but became a good friend and was such a hardworking nurse. She was precise at everything. Never ask her the time as it would be the exact minutes and seconds, which was slightly odd.

I put my all into this job I loved it so much. I would always be there half an hour before I was meant to be and never left until I was sure everything was safe and the staff were OK. This was my dream job and I was going to give it my everything; I was so happy and it showed.

Abby was an enrolled nurse who was almost orange where she spent so long in the sun and was involved with a married policeman long term which didn't seem to be going anywhere. She was very set in her ways and worked every weekend to get maximum pay but was very capable and reliable.

Ann was another of my staff nurses who was a sweet girl but unfortunately, couldn't control her diabetes very well so we had to keep a close eye on her. Sara was quite new to the ward she moved to the area from Nottingham with her fiancé they were planning a wedding.

The ward clerk, Rose, was a fiery tyrant of a woman and she tried to rule everyone so we had to have some ground rules early on. It seemed the rest of my staff were very junior and wanted to find their professional feet and were very responsive to learning and being mentored.

Every time I came on duty, I went to each and every patient to speak with them to see how they were and how things were generally. I was always accessible to all patients and staff and that's exactly how I wanted it. The staff found it initially strange as my predecessor spent all her time in the office and didn't get involved with patient care, which reading this you will find astonishing I certainly did.

Tia, one of the junior staff nurses, came running to find me. I was testing urine in the sluice and she was ashen. She mumbled that one of the patients was unresponsive and barely breathing. No doctors were responding when the emergency bleep was sent out. I ran out to see one of our young female patients, as she described. Her blood pressure was low and I asked Tia to urgently check her blood sugar. It was unrecordable.

I asked for a cannula (the fine plastic tube which goes into a vein), a fifty-millilitre syringe and glucose. I went into emergency mode as my staff stood watching me put the cannula into the vein and inject the glucose into the patient.

Slowly, she responded and her blood sugars were back to normal she was fine. The staff were so pleased but as they were chatting, Butch walked in asking what was going on.

It was explained to her and she looked at me saying you shouldn't have done that you could be disciplined! I looked at her saying disciplined for saving someone's life? Please do it if you have to I am happy to answer for my actions. I turned and walked away; I could feel all eyes on me, but it was never mentioned again.

The consultants were all so different which was an enjoyable challenge, it made ward rounds on a Monday morning a guessing game 'Who would be in what mood?' One of my consultants was a dapper chap silk handkerchief always in the top pocket matching tie and socks. Always smelled of expensive cologne and was so well turned out. He loved gossip and always asked me what was new, hoping for some juicy story which more often than not didn't get.

He saw his patients whilst reading yesterday's Sunday paper and always turned to the pages where the swimsuit models could be found. He certainly loved the ladies. He was a great surgeon in his sub-speciality but was highly sought after to teach all over the world so we didn't often see him, his senior registrar held the reins.

We were fortunate to have two professors and they were also excellent surgeons and real consultants who led the team from the front. At this point in my career, I felt that all the eight consultants I had the privilege of working alongside were supportive, patient centred and all round good people as well as being excellent surgeons. Things changed as time went on and not always for the better. Some of our juniors were characters too.

Dr Ravensbury, a tall Oxford graduate who spoke with the most educated of English accents, was the funniest. At the end of my ward was a fire escape which we sometimes used to take shortcuts to the other block of wards it was convenient and certainly not putting anyone in danger. He came to me one day saying, 'Sister, may I slip down your back passage?' This caused a roar of laughter from all the patients and staff and gave me huge red cheeks with embarrassment. Funny now, though.

There were many ground breaking treatments being developed and I was proud to be involved in these. As a team, we did things together and one particular incident springs to mind, which left us all feeling a little "uncomfortable", to say the least. Some of our procedures required bowel prep which is a medication which cleans the bowel out and allows the surgeon an unobstructed view and clear path on which to operate.

This was in the form of a very explosive drink. We all decided to try it just to understand what our patients experienced. Four of us took just half a sachet each, patients were expected to drink a whole one on three consecutive days. I was the first to feel the wrath of this during my tea break where I had to run like an Olympic athlete to the toilet in mid-sentence almost knocking over everyone over in my way. It was like an explosion.

One by one, we experienced its effects. Abby seemed not to have any effect from it until just before the end of her shift. She felt the rumblings but nothing was happening. I suggested she took a bedpan home with her in the car. Thank goodness she did as it was put to good use almost all the way home in the front of a mini! Never did we try anything like this again!

The ward had several specialities which was an excellent place for learning opportunities for nurses and doctors but it could be an organisational nightmare at times. I always have enjoyed a challenge so soaked it all up ensuring that every patient and visitor had exceptional care and attention and never allowing standards to fall.

We frequently had staff coming into the ward to see our patients as many had had innovative surgery. This wasn't acceptable unless it had been cleared by the consultant or myself. Patients had to be protected, learning came second. I remember one incident where a very junior doctor (house officer) came onto the ward and went straight into my office and started going through the notes trolley.

I walked in. He didn't acknowledge me, so I challenged as to why he was there. He informed me that his father was one of the consultants on another ward so he decided it would be good to take the opportunity to find out what was going on. I told him to leave the ward as I would not allow him to disturb my patients; he had no right to even be on the ward. He became extremely obnoxious and abusive, saying his father would have something to say, how dare I say this to him. He wasn't leaving, I would not back down.

He did leave eventually after some of my team came to see what the commotion was. My concern was how junior he was and how he would progress into being unbearable and a potential bully and all the staff he may upset or even destroy in the future as it seemed his path was set and he may not even make a good doctor but felt it his right. It was obvious he felt superior to a mere nurse and was also a privileged brat that needed sorting out!

There had been several medical students who felt it necessary to "look down" on the nursing staff but were given a sharp lesson by my team they were learning well and I was proud of who they were. They were all growing before my eyes where previously they were somewhat suppressed and kept on a short leash they were expected to be subservient, not with me, I wanted them to question, to challenge and to learn and they were certainly doing that.

On a late shift, Ann was feeling unwell so I suggested she called her boyfriend to take her home. Her diabetes was more unstable of late so I was concerned and felt she needed a review from her consultant. She left the ward around eight in the evening, assuring me her boyfriend was outside and she would get an urgent appointment with her consultant. I felt reassured by this and said I would call her later in the evening.

Around nine-thirty that evening I had a phone call from Ann who had felt a little lightheaded on the way home and said she had been attacked, she was crying on the phone. I tried to find out where she was, she hadn't left the hospital grounds and was in the back of the little car park away from the main area. I immediately rang security to meet me and we ran to where she was. We found her in the undergrowth half-dressed and bleeding.

I called the police to attend urgently and an ambulance. An ambulance has to be called even on hospital grounds, that is the way it is. I comforted her, she was conscious but badly injured. I stayed with her and wouldn't leave her side. Her boyfriend came, but she didn't call him to collect her. She thought she would be all right on her own. Her family lived in the northwest of Scotland and she didn't want them to be contacted.

Ann had been raped. It transpired that she was attacked by another nurse who was working for the agency at the hospital. Ann recognised him and told me what had happened. The police were so considerate and gentle with her. Ann was a determined girl who was not going to allow this man to do this to her. She was prepared to work tirelessly with the police to get this man arrested.

All the checks swabs, etc., had to be taken before anything further could happen. I stayed with Ann until four in the morning and then took her home with me to my home. I couldn't let her be alone. I had phoned home to explain there was a problem and Ann would be coming home with me. Will was happy with this but obviously concerned.

We eventually got home and I sat up with Ann, just talking. Her bruised face and cuts over her neck were so very apparent she even had a deep bite mark on her inner thigh, it must have been just awful for her. I had to organise for her insulin to be delivered to me, she didn't have any at all but my friend who was also a hospital emergency department consultant sorted that really quickly and it came in a taxi to us.

I set about getting her into bed and then thought that she couldn't be left whilst I went to work. As luck would have it, I was on a study day the following day so called in the first thing to say I couldn't attend. No reason was given. I then called Mrs Butcher to tell her I would need a couple of days off. Initially, it was not received well but then she softened and realised the severity of the issue. Ann's parents were making their way to us so they could take her home for a while to rest and recover.

The police had arrested someone for the attack and were coming around to see Ann that afternoon. She was shaken but remained strong. The police arrived and discussed what they had done. Ann wanted me to be present and I sat and held her hand, not saying anything unless asked to. The agency nurse had been suspended from the General Nursing Council, the GNC (as it was then, now NMC, Nursing and Midwifery Council) for sexual abuse of a colleague. He was never charged by the police but was suspended and had only in the past few months gone back on the register to be able to work as a registered nurse.

We were all shocked by this information and also that it would be a prosecution if Ann agreed. She didn't hesitate, absolutely prosecute, he can't do this to anyone else.

Ann's parents took her home with them the next day, where she stayed for three months. On her return, I ensured she worked alongside me on every shift, making sure she was supported and feeling safe. This worked for her well and she remained strong. The trial happened several months later, I attended with her and he was convicted of rape and serious assault, sentenced to eight years in prison and this time finally struck off of the register. Not before time.

The governing body of my profession has a lot to answer for. This could have been avoided should they have taken previous allegations more seriously. Ann was never the same after her attack, she became continuously nervous when on her own, her boyfriend couldn't cope with how she was feeling and he blamed himself for not being there when this dreadful thing happened, so they split up.

She stayed with us on the team as that was the only place she felt safe and it had stability. She later moved in with some other nurses, so she wasn't living alone. Her life took more than ten years to gain some normality, being there for her was of paramount importance, we still are in contact to this day.

Our team was very close, even June our housekeeper was a close part of the team and was involved in all our social events and ward meetings. I and the team were there for her when her husband passed away, she was part of us and we were such a supportive and tight family, so it was natural. This had never happened with my predecessor and it took everyone who had worked with her a while to adjust but it was a huge success and the staff loved the inclusion and were so responsive and involved bringing us all even closer.

We interviewed for a nursing auxiliary (N/A) to join our existing team of nursing assistants who were invaluable. Jim and I employed a bubbly woman in her mid-thirties who had previously worked in a nursing home and came with excellent references and she seemed to be a great fit for the team.

Jim was going to take her under his very experienced wing to ensure she was supported and prepared for the busy and demanding job ahead. We were pleased with the appointment of Paula and everything seemed to be on course. I was unprepared for the months ahead.

Butch was retiring from her post and we all had a big celebration there was laughter and tears but she had a great send-off. We would miss her but she had given her all to her job and deserved her retirement. A new nursing officer had been appointed to the post who had come from the private sector and had moved around quite a lot. She hadn't worked in the NHS for many years and had limited experience of being a 'hands-on' nurse.

The ward sisters and charge nurses of the surgical floor were called to meet Catriona Ballom-Jewkes. We all walked in to be greeted by a stone-faced woman with a pinched look and her handbag over her crooked left arm just as Mrs Thatcher wore hers. She was extremely upright and immaculately turned out. There was no emotion or warmth on her face, as we were all individually introduced to her.

She looked each one of us up and down and announced she would want to see us separately in her office to tell us her plans. We were slightly taken aback as she had no idea of what the unit was about and what we had achieved and she was about to set new goals without due consideration to the situation as a whole.

There were twelve ward sisters/charge nurses who were all feeling uneasy with what was ahead. She had an unnerving presence and was making us all feel on edge but why we weren't sure.

Each one of us was given time to go and see her where she addressed us formally and we had to address her by her full name and we were never to use her Christian name that was the first thing she said to each one of us. Her stand-offish attitude was almost hostile, I felt, although she seemed to have a favourite in the only charge nurse on the unit as her attitude was much softer which was slightly puzzling.

It was my turn and she sat behind her desk, which was neat and tidy and no visible work piles just the file on my ward. I walked in and she told me to "sit", no eye contact, no welcoming or warmth; I felt deeply uncomfortable. Her first words to me were, 'I was spending too much money from the budget on drugs and dressings. I reminded her we were a huge surgical ward of forty-six beds so we would use an enormous amount of consumables and drugs.'

How did she propose I change it? Her answer was to close the beds. How could we do this when we had ninety-nine per cent bed occupancy? Cancel surgery was her answer, I was astounded. She seemed so sure this was the answer and said I had to do this to get the budget back on track for the whole of the unit, something which had never been an issue before her arrival.

My ward had been chosen by her, as it was the largest. Some of my staff would then be redeployed to other areas, which again was a huge blow. My team would be devastated. My ward budget was always on track and never had I been advised there was an issue it was a complete surprise and I wasn't quite sure what on earth was going on here as we were such a busy ward and our waiting lists were vast, we had a problem keeping up with things now.

I was conscious that I was being stared at in an almost angry way. I asked what I was supposed to do. I would need help and her advice but had to voice that I felt it would be to the detriment of the patients, many of whom were cancer patients waiting for urgent surgery. The reply I got made me feel ill and I could feel my face flushing with anger.

I was told at this meeting that whatever was needed to get the expenditure down, then it would be done and if it meant patients suffering a "little", then so be it. I stood up and said, 'I'm sorry I do not agree with patients suffering from inefficiencies in the system.'

We seemed to be inheriting more managers and less clinical staff and this was a change in service, at a cost which was impacting the patients. I was told in a very angry way that it was going to happen and that whatever she requested, it would be obeyed and never questioned. I was in a red mist and not thinking clearly. I asked if the consultants had been consulted? No, as it wasn't their call, apparently they would be "dealt" with in due course.

Well, that was something which would cause a huge explosion with the consultants and rightly so they would not be accepting of this, that's for sure. I was advised to leave as my time with her was over.

How this woman could ever have been a nurse was beyond me; also she had been in post just a couple of weeks and had no clue of how things really worked. I was devastated but didn't want her to see me cry. I walked out, not saying a word and went into the toilet and sobbed. Patients and my staff were of equal importance to me and I had no idea that this was coming.

Chapter Five

I got back to the ward red-eyed and went into my office to try
to calm down. Rose came to talk to me and could see I was
upset. She went to make me a cup of tea and asked me if I was
all right and was there if I needed her. She didn't press me and
I didn't say what the issue was.

I composed myself and went looking for Jim; he was
going through ward policies with Paula, I was told. I had
difficulty locating him but eventually found him in the old
teaching room right at the back of the ward, which we never
used. I opened the door and was greeted with the sight of Jim
and Paula wrapped around each other, obviously not just
talking.

Today was not the day to test my patience as I asked what
did they think they were doing? They both pulled their clothes
together and said they were sorry and it just happened. This
was something I disbelieved. It was more than that. I looked
at Jim saying do you realise what you are doing?

My head was spinning. I couldn't go to speak to my new
manager. She was unapproachable and would relish the fact
that she could discipline staff, I was sure of that. I told Jim to
go back to work and spoke with Paula. I advised her that she
couldn't work on this ward in the circumstances so I would

arrange for her to work in another area so they would not be in the same place. I sent her off to the library to think about what she had done whilst I think about what I needed to do.

I called another unit's nursing officer who was a sensible approachable nurse who would advise me. Lorna listened as I told her the events of the day and slumped back in her chair in disbelief. She remained professional but knew me well as I cared for her father, so we did have a bond.

As far as the issue with Mrs Ballom-Jewkes (Mrs B-J), she suggested I discuss it with the consultants, which I had planned to do and take my lead from them. This issue with Jim and Paula was somewhat different. They needed to be suspended at worst at best redeployment as I had suggested. Jim had a wife and child and Paula was living with her fiancé and they had three children.

Lorna could see I was in turmoil and extremely upset by the day's events so said she would take this over. She was senior even to Mrs B-J so was able to make these decisions. I was relieved, I will be honest I wasn't sure if I could cope with what was happening at the same time and was angry with Jim and Mrs B-J for different reasons.

I got back to the ward and Jim came rushing to me, asking me not to tell his wife. I put my hand out to stop him talking and said that was his job, not mine; no one would hear anything from me. I told him I was waiting to hear what was to happen, as I had spoken to Lorna. He pleaded with me to halt anything but I couldn't ignore what was happening. It could seriously affect the care of patients and couldn't happen.

I shut myself in my office to try to get my thoughts together. The phone rang and it was Lorna. She said Jim would need to be suspended and Paula also. She would be along with a member of staff from personnel (Human Resources, as it is now known) to do this. I felt deflated everything seemed to be happening around me.

The staff were very quiet after Jim and Paula's suspension and advised me that they were having an affair for some time. I had no idea.

Mrs B-J came to find me a few days after this event as she was away and was angry that she wasn't the first person to be informed. She started to lecture me and talk down to me. I felt like a naughty small child being scolded.

I let her carry on until she finished. I then said this is why I didn't tell you because you have no compassion and no idea of how to manage or guide staff. I feel that I can't approach you or confide in you, as you always seem so hostile to me and I just don't know why. I was calm and polite but had to say what I did. I will never forget the look on her face when I was talking to her she was livid with me. I thought I have done it now, she will never let this go.

Things went quiet for a while, Jim was given a written warning and was lucky to keep his job after four weeks of being suspended. Unfortunately, he didn't keep his marriage. His wife left him taking their daughter with her. Paula resigned from her post before even getting to a disciplinary hearing. No one heard from her again. Jim returned to work and remained very reserved but he was an exceptional nurse so he resumed his senior position as there was no question of his capabilities.

I had as little to do with Mrs B-J as possible but had to continue a working relationship and be professional. I had spoken with the consultants who told me to carry on as I always had and protect our patients, which I certainly would do.

I hadn't closed any beds despite being initially told to do so, as we were swamped with patients every day. The emergency department had no place to send acute surgical patients if we closed beds so I kept them open. I do think on reflection that I was slowly creating my own destiny but my own morals would not allow it any other way.

The Gulf War was in full swing and I was advised that twenty of my beds had been designated as receiving beds for injured service personnel. It was mayhem, twenty of my beds were removed and in came new electric beds with water mattresses. New chairs, monitors for every bed infusion pumps and every gadget you could think of was being delivered. We weren't allowed to use these beds or equipment for anything but military patients.

The ward was quickly turned into a mini-intensive care unit and we then waited anxiously hoping we wouldn't have injured military coming through the doors; we didn't know what to expect, especially as so much money had been put into the ward. We were also told we would have soldiers stationed on the wards, which was alien to us and a little unnerving. Our cars were checked to ensure no devices had been placed on our vehicles, it was a scary time.

We continued on and had to work extra shifts and hours to keep up with a bigger turnover of patients as they weren't staying in as long as usual so we could get more through the system and ensure waiting lists didn't go up. I constantly battled with Mrs B-J over budget but we had to use what was needed for safety purposes and the needs of the patients. I was exhausted not getting days off together and working sometimes fourteen-hour days as my staff were also on their knees so I wanted to protect them too.

In the middle of all the mayhem, I went to the staff restaurant on my break with a couple of the nurses and saw Mark looking over at me. I thought my legs were about to give way. I felt my head spinning and my face was hot and flushed. He walked over to me, smiling, saying he had been trying to find me.

We sat and talked for a while and he asked me if I would consider starting our relationship again. I still had very strong feelings for him but had put them to the back of my mind, although I thought of him often. With tears in my eyes, I said I couldn't do that and we shouldn't see each other again.

'He was very upset and pleaded for me to reconsider,' I said, 'no, I did care about him but I also cared deeply for my family, that was the last time I set eyes on him but know he is now married with four children and a respected GP in Cornwall. I will always have deep feelings for him.'

Jim was still with me but quiet. We never discussed the incident again. I had come onto a late shift an hour early like I always did when Jim rushed to see me. Can you call Sara urgently? She is trying to get hold of you. Sara was a staff nurse who was planning her wedding and was so excited she was not from the area, so we were her helpers locally. The ward truly was a close family looking out for each other.

I dialled her number and a voice answered. I didn't recognise. I asked to speak with her. It was a police officer I was speaking with. Sara came to the phone and was speaking with a quivering voice and sobbing in between words. Eventually, I heard her say he is gone.

My first thoughts were, *Oh, no, they have ended the relationship,* if only that had been true. Sara had gone to the supermarket early that morning and left her fiancé in bed. When she came back, she found him hanging from the loft, he had taken his own life.

I could not imagine the shock that poor girl faced when she got home. She just kept saying, 'I will be in as soon as I can,' as she was due on the late shift with me. I kept telling her no, she wasn't to come to work and I would be there as soon as I could. I then spoke to the police officer who advised that her sister was on the way. She didn't live too far just a couple of hours away.

I felt helpless. I wanted to help her but nothing I could do from the ward. I called Mrs B-J to tell her what had happened. Her compassion as always was totally missing, all she could say was, 'Well, you will have to cover the shifts. There's no spare staff.' No mention of Sara or any sign of concern. I really didn't understand this woman and had never met anyone like her before.

We were down staff with leave already booked so we just had to knuckle down and get things done. I left the ward after a horrendous and long shift of almost twelve hours, realising, I had only managed a few sips of water and never even managed to go to the loo!

I went straight to Sara after calling Will to say what I was doing. He was, as always, understanding and supportive. I stayed for about an hour as Sara's sister and brother-in-law were there, so I felt I didn't want to intrude. She wasn't going to be alone and was going to stay with her sister. I told her we would talk when she was ready.

I had to do extra shifts to cover and I went for over a month without a day off. I wasn't able to get any time back as we didn't have cover; it was a never-ending battle but we kept at it.

We had a registrar (a junior doctor, who was not far from becoming a consultant), who was a nice enough chap but extremely eccentric and a little strange. He used to come to the ward and wanting to talk to me. When I was on in the evenings, he always brought me a chocolate éclair as he had heard it was my favourite and he would make me a cup of tea. He didn't seem to have friends or a social life so I would sit and talk to him, general chit-chat.

He was a portly chap and had a tight shirt and trousers always. He sat at the desk talking to me whilst I was writing up notes. I glanced up as I was talking occasionally. On one occasion, I looked up and noticed he had an enormous erection and he didn't try to hide it. I carried on talking about nonsense. I'm sure it was when he then asked me to go out to dinner with him as he had wanted to do this for a long time as he had strong feelings for me.

I stood up and walked towards the door saying, 'Thank you but I don't think my husband would be too pleased. It would be good to be friends.' I left him in the office and he avoided coming to the ward when I was on duty after this. I was concerned for him but could not risk any form of encouragement.

Thankfully, as in all rotations during training, they move hospitals fairly frequently and he moved to another teaching hospital within a few months. I did feel sorry for him and hoped he would be happy in the future.

I was close to breaking point with all what had happened and I had no support from my manager. It was extremely testing for me as a nurse and as a person. I was concerned that I was in a vulnerable place and didn't want a repeat of my previous meltdown and almost destroying my personal life. The good thing I was aware.

Sara never did come back to the ward. She couldn't cope with caring for anyone and she was an excellent nurse, so very sad on so many levels. She is now working for a large department store as a Human Resources manager in London.

I had a well-earned and long overdue weekend off coming up and I was so looking forward to it after all the extra hours I had been doing. I needed time with my family. We had on the ward a man who had had a life-changing surgical procedure which involved him having not only a colostomy bag but amputation of his penis and scrotum.

He was due to get married the following year but because of his prognosis was bringing the wedding forward to three weeks' time. This was devastating for him as it would any man. He was only thirty-four years of age. He didn't mix with any of the other patients and only myself and the surgeon were privileged to have seen the results of the surgery he would not allow anyone else to look.

I sat talking to him numerous times during his stay and did all his dressings and taught him how to change his colostomy bag. He trusted me and that was important for his recovery.

He was told he was able to go home on the coming Saturday the day his stitches were due out. I was a day off and he was devastated that either he couldn't go home or the stitches would have to be removed by someone else. He had a great trust in me and I felt I was almost letting him down by being off; I told him not to worry, I would just pop in and take them out. He was delighted and started to cry.

It was all arranged and I came in on a Saturday morning, took out the stitches, documented what I had done and left. He was able to go home and was happy and grateful for the care he had received. I came back in for a late shift on the following Tuesday, not giving a second thought to coming in. I didn't log it as time at work nor was I going to claim time or money, as it was a gesture of goodwill and caring for my patient.

I came in and was immediately told that I had to go to see Mrs B J. It was urgent. Slightly concerned, I went straight to her office where she was sitting looking stone-faced. I went in and said that she had wanted to see me urgently. She had the most evil look in her eyes I think I had ever come across; she lunged forward as she spoke to me, saying I was irresponsible, self-gratifying and a disgrace as a ward sister.

I was lost for words and this was a bolt out of the blue. My mind was racing I was thinking, *what have I done? Had I given the wrong medication? Had I upset staff patients or visitors?* 'What have I done?' I asked, totally unaware of what she was talking about.

She then said, 'I had no right to prioritise patients and to come in on my time off to give special treatment just to take stitches out!' I was getting more angry and red in the face, I thought I was going to explode.

I raised my voice and said, 'Do you really believe what you're saying is true or even helpful to this patient who had undergone drastic surgery just to give him a slightly longer life which, in fact, might only be a few months and your concerned that I came into help him. I cannot believe you are saying this to me, I am a nurse and always will care.'

Her face was puckered and red and she shouted at me saying, 'The problem with you is you care too much.' This was unbelievable.

I replied, 'The problem with you is you don't care at all, you're a disgrace.'

I was never so angry and I just stared at her. I never forget the look on her face as she had a wry smile and said, 'I will have you for this. You can be sure. Just wait and see.' She really hated me and had done so from the start.

'Do your worst but I won't be the person you want me to be just because you want it.'

I turned and walked away, going straight back to the ward and crying in my office through sheer anger. I wasn't going to let her change me or my attitude no one had ever said anything like this to me before. I didn't tell the staff but did confide in a friend who was another ward sister. She was aware of Mrs B J's animosity towards me. I also logged it as I just didn't trust her.

We carried on the day-to-day runnings of the ward and it was as busy as ever. We were told that we were getting a visit from a royal who was coming to open a new wing in the hospital. We were so very excited. We weren't told who it was because of security and had visits from several security personnel so we assumed they were coming to our ward as not every ward had the inspections.

All the staff wanted to work that day so we had to do juggling of the rota to allow it to happen. I was given the surgical floor bleep that day to cover the whole of the unit, which was strange, as it wasn't my turn.

We had heard just an hour before that it was Princess Diana, so we were even more excited. I was going around the ward making sure everything was in order and saw her getting out of a car through the window; she was radiant. I knew she was due to be with us in fifteen minutes so ensured I looked professional and had butterflies.

About five minutes before she was due, the emergency bleep went off to say I was needed urgently on a ward which was the furthest from where I was. I couldn't believe it. I ran out of the ward and ran down the corridor, having to run straight past the royal visitor and her party of hangers on. Mrs B J was one of those and she should have had the bleep, not me, as that was her job.

I felt really stupid apologising as I ran through. I heard the princess say 'I hope she is all right, what's happening?'

I got to the ward unable to breathe as it was quite a distance. The staff nurse looked at me, saying that she just wanted a drug check but it wasn't due for another hour. Mrs B J said she would sort it with me. I realised she had done this to me on purpose. I checked the drug with the staff nurse as I was there and made my way back, walking this time quite quickly as I was furious.

I got just outside the ward next door to mine and saw that the royal party was just leaving my ward. The princess glanced in my direction and saw me, then told the party to hold on, she wanted to speak with me. Mrs B J was livid and you could see she wanted to stop this from happening.

The princess walked towards me and stopped to talk to me, putting her hand on my arm. She was, without doubt, a beautiful woman inside and out. We talked for around five minutes. What we said will always be my secret but she knew enough about me by the end of it to hug me as she left. She turned as she walked away and smiled at me. My eyes were full of tears, this time with joy.

I went back to my ward feeling elated to the staff telling me what I had missed for me to tell them what had happened. We were all buzzing with excitement. Mrs B J came to the ward about an hour later and said I acted recklessly and didn't keep to protocol and made a laughingstock of the entire hospital. I stood looking at her, still smiling, which annoyed her even more, saying, 'Did you get a personal chat or a hug? NO, I don't suppose you did!' I turned and walked away saying I have patients to attend to.

The ward was busy every day and yet again. We had to work extra hours to keep things ticking over. All my staff got overtime payments. I didn't really bother; just took an odd day off if I could, which was rare. I was advised by one of the other nursing officers that I should start to put it on my time sheet.

The relationship with Mrs B J was fraught and it was obvious how she felt about me to everyone, however when she was around senior managers, she was pleasant to me almost gushing but never when there were junior members of staff only. At any meetings she wouldn't give me any eye contact or tried her best not to bring me into the conversation, so many of my colleagues noticed it and they were oblivious to anything that had gone on between us.

This was my downfall. I didn't reveal our difficult relationship to my peers. I didn't feel it appropriate to do so. I did start to log all our conversations and meetings and was always conscious I wanted a third person present when with her. I did not trust her one bit but was guilty I felt this way as I shouldn't.

Each month, I went through staff time sheets and signed them off. Mine went in with all the others unsigned to the central office. I had been including all my extra hours for around 4 months now and my sheet came back with the others bearing a signature. I didn't ever look at the signature, it was always the same one so it didn't raise any concerns for me.

Life was busy and I felt at times I was drowning in other's problems, not patients but staff. Whatever was thrown at me, I dealt with and didn't look to anyone for help and we, as a team, worked through our issues. Our patients got the best care possible and we were faced with some difficult conditions to treat we were a regional centre for our speciality so very experienced in caring for complex patients.

On arrival on shift one day I was handed over the patients and overnight we had admitted a man who was said to be gravely ill, vomiting fresh blood (haematemesis) and passing it through his urine (haematuria). The night staff were concerned about him but said he was stable. I always went around to speak to every patient at the beginning of each shift to get an idea of how they were physically and mentally.

I got to Mr A and he was sitting up in bed looking alert and well. I spoke with him and he changed, saying he felt unwell and thought he was dying. His pulse and blood pressure were normal as were all his blood tests. He was a man who concerned me not because he was physically ill but psychologically, I felt.

I suggested he go out to the bathroom so we could see how he felt. One of the nurses went with him and I suggested he might like a bath to freshen up and we would change his bedding. He thought that was a good idea, so off I went to get his wash things from his locker. As I was doing this, the emergency bell went off in the bathroom. I got him his wash things and ran with them in hand to the bathroom where he was on the floor covered in blood. He wasn't responding.

I threw his wash bag across the room. It hit the wall and landed on a chair. As we were trying to get him stable, one of the nurses said to look at the chair under the washbag, it was covered in blood. We were all bemused by what was happening. Our junior doctor arrived and I went to the bag to see what had happened. Imagine my shock to find plastic bags full of blood inside!

Mr A wasn't unwell at all but had Munchausen Syndrome (a condition where symptoms are made up to get medical attention). He had scars over his abdomen where surgery had been carried out in various hospitals. We found out that he was known well to many hospitals and had had numerous procedures, but nothing had ever been found to be wrong.

I had never come across this before, it was a steep learning curve for us all. Psychiatric care was needed urgently for this man. It transpired that he had numerous bags of rabbit's blood amongst his belongings and if his wash bag hadn't been dropped, he would have possibly had another surgical procedure.

He was transferred to psychiatry to get the care he desperately needed. The staff were stunned at this, just how convincing everything was. We all learnt a valuable lesson.

Chapter Six

In two years, we had very little sickness or absence amongst the staff and the turnover was almost non-existent. The team was solid and close no one wanted to leave but many wanted to come and work with us. I was the happiest I could be in my role with just the one exception of Mrs B J.

We tended to stay away from each other as much as possible; it suited me but there are times when you need your manager for advice and support. I needed support when one of my team, Karen came to speak to me after her night shift she looked ashen and was trembling. I sat her down and moved closer to her as I felt she needed some support.

She started to tell me that she had started a relationship with one of the patients who had been on the ward a few months back and it was serious they wanted to get married. She was afraid as we would all know he was an ex-patient. They wanted to get married as soon as possible as his prognosis was poor and they felt they didn't have much time together so there was some urgency.

Karen sobbed as she told me and I cried with her. I was in turmoil as I wasn't sure if she had overstepped a professional line but was clearly distressed. I will admit it was one of the toughest issues I had ever faced. I asked Karen to be honest with me when I asked if the relationship started whilst she was caring for him on the ward.

She said it hadn't started at that point but they both wanted it to happen and it didn't start until a few weeks after he had been discharged. I was relieved at this. I told her that any unprofessional behaviour would be severely frowned upon and would be disciplinary action. She promised that that was never the case and, in fact, she ensured she didn't care for him directly when on duty.

We decided that it was all above board and there was nothing to answer for and the main thing was getting them to their wedding and keeping health and happiness at the forefront. Karen was relieved and was happy that she could take it forward and organise things as quickly as possible. Some of the staff were aware of the relationship and could back up what she had told me. I hugged her tight and said I would help her with whatever she needed.

The ward remained fairly manic every day and we carried on with caring for our patients. Most of the staff were working extra hours and that included me. I came onto a late shift to find Mrs B J waiting with a smug look on her face, she was sitting at my desk and in the corner, I noticed, that there was a senior Human Resources (HR) manager sat in the corner that smiled at me as I walked into the office.

I said hello to them both. No greeting back and was told I was suspended with immediate effect and to leave the premises. I was stunned and felt the room spinning around me. I had no idea what was going on. I was asked for the keys to my personal drawer, which I refused to give as I had no idea what was going on. Mrs B J stood up and pointed to the door, saying leave now, her face almost delighted.

I looked around and couldn't see any of my team; I protested saying what about the cover for the patients. 'That isn't important, this is, so leave,' she said, raising her voice.

I had no choice but to go. I went back to my car and was shaking, confused and felt sick. I immediately rang the Royal College of Nursing (RCN) and asked for the senior officer. He came on the phone and I was relieved to hear a voice I had known for many years. I started to tell him what had happened and he said he would come to see me at home the next day.

I drove home in a daze. I felt ashamed but didn't know why. I got home but didn't remember actually driving through the familiar places and slumped in the chair and started to sob. I rang Will, babbling and he was really worried so said he would come straight home. He arrived and we went over what had happened.

He took over, saying, right, this has been coming for some time, it's a personal vendetta, no question. She won't get away with this we needed to get all the evidence together. I rang some of my team, it was strange that I couldn't actually get to speak to them with one exception. It was Karen who said they had been told that they weren't allowed to speak with me at all, they had been threatened by Mrs B J if they did, they would be disciplined. I was stunned. I wasn't about to put any of the staff in a difficult position so said that was fine.

I couldn't sleep, I couldn't eat. My world had finally caved in on me.

Phil, the RCN senior officer, arrived the next day to see me, I was eagerly awaiting him. He said he had been in touch with the HR manager and I was being accused of fraud for signing my own timesheet and claiming for hours I hadn't worked. I was outraged.

I had been telling everyone what was happening and had so many witnesses and evidence of my work. Phil was supportive and said this woman is definitely 'out to get you', so we need to build a solid case and turn the tables.

It seemed like a lifetime until I actually had anything in writing stating what I was accused of. The letter said that I was suspended and awaiting further investigation, which was ongoing. I spoke with Phil and asked him if we need to speak with any further legal representation. As the issue was around the signature on my timesheet, Will suggested we employ a handwriting expert to look at the timesheets.

Phil agreed it would be a good idea and the RCN would fund this. This seemed a great idea and Phil would get straight into it. There was a meeting scheduled for six weeks away to meet with management and have the disciplinary procedure.

I was left in limbo, I didn't want to go out as I felt so ashamed as I felt everyone assumed I had done wrong, which obviously wasn't the case. I was a strong person and used this negative time to turn this into a time where I put my case together, the evidence that I had gathered and to get my own thoughts channelled towards resolving this. Every waking hour was consumed by this and the need to prove my innocence.

I had frequent calls with the RCN and met with a solicitor and handwriting expert who was employed by the Crown Court so was extremely experienced. I had to produce as much evidence of my signature going back ten years as I could possibly find, so we could present the best possible case. I even phoned the police to explain what had happened and they didn't want to know, saying it wasn't seen as a criminal offence and was employment related.

Being busy helped me focus, I still wasn't sleeping and I had lost an enormous amount of weight. My family was worried about me and I didn't want that to happen my parents were angry that this was happening to me but felt helpless, as did Will, who was my rock.

My GP came to see me and wanted to give me antidepressants. I refused. I wanted to do this myself. She was supportive and said she was there if I needed her. The day of the meeting finally came around. Will wanted to come with me but I didn't want him there as I could see him losing his temper and that would be too stressful for me.

Phil picked me up and we drove to the hospital I was together but inside was in shreds I didn't want to show this. We waited to go into the boardroom and seemed to wait for what seemed like hours.

Eventually in we went and there were five senior managers sitting around the huge table. I sat at the other end with Phil. I felt all the eyes penetrating through me; I felt I had been convicted already. The proceedings started and there didn't seem to be anything concrete, just the signature query. The only witness that was called for management was Mrs B J, who obviously had an issue and was mentioning anything she could to try to discredit me.

She was asked if my clinical judgement was under question, she became flustered and answered that I appeared to get 'too' involved in the care of patients. Phil took her to task; on this, she was becoming more and more angry with every sentence, it was too obvious she had a big problem with me as an individual.

I had a string of witnesses whom all upheld my dedication and professionalism without any question. The professor of surgery came and spoke very highly of me, which brought me to tears. Phil squeezed my arm both in support and to ensure I stayed strong. I looked into the faces of each individual on the panel, they couldn't look me in the eye; I sensed there was an element of unease in two of the panel and I wasn't sure what was going on.

The professor said he was astounded that this was being allowed to happen as clearly "management was inept" as there was a witch hunt going on, he was furious. Well, the elephant in the room was addressed, my mouth fell open. The chairwoman who was the head of surgical services, a non-clinical person, I might add, was not at all happy. She stated that she was in full support of her manager Mrs B J and this would be resolved today. My stomach turned somersaults, I didn't know what to expect.

The question was then raised about the signature on my time sheet. No one had admitted to it being theirs, so I had to have signed this fraudulently myself. I looked at Phil, who produced six copies of a detailed report from the Graphologist (forensic handwriting expert). It was seven pages in length with various forms of my signature from documents over the past ten years, more than forty-five of my specimen signatures on existing documents.

There was also a sample of all the nursing officers and anyone who signed the sheets, again on existing documents so they couldn't be altered. The report categorically stated I had not signed the sheet. There were no characteristics remotely similar to my own documents. However, there were some similarities in one of the signatures of a nursing officer. It was Mrs B J.

The panel looked very uneasy and the chairwoman was frantically searching through the document to find if she could come back with any counterargument. We were asked to leave the room at this point. We had been outside for around an hour and saw two of the panel leaving, not looking in our direction at all; I didn't know what this meant but felt more nauseated than before.

We eventually went in and sat down. The chairwoman said that she was convinced that I had signed my own time sheets to claim fraudulently against the hospital and I had been a difficult person to manage by Mrs B J and it was her opinion that I should be removed from my post.

The room started to spin, I had done nothing wrong and I knew this was just the worst outcome ever. I loved every aspect of my job and would have never ever done anything illegal. Phil started to argue the fact that the evidence was overwhelming in my favour and if they felt it was a matter of fraud, it must be reported to the police.

I remember nodding frantically, almost begging them to do so. It was said they didn't think it necessary to do so and a dismissal was all that was required. I stood up and left, needing to get some air. Phil was left in the room with the chairwoman. A member of the panel walked out in front of me and walked towards me, her eyes filled with tears saying, 'I'm truly sorry, I really am.'

I found this extremely strange. She walked off, saying nothing else. Phil eventually came out and stood with me, saying this was a disgrace, a witch-hunt morally and professionally wrong. He could not believe it. Apparently, the chairwoman's words were, 'I have to support my manager.'

with no thought to me who had worked there for several years and was unblemished in her record.

As we looked, we saw Mrs B J and the chairwoman coming out of the back entrance laughing and joking together, it was rubbing salt into my very open wound.

I went home knowing I wouldn't be going back to what I loved and was so very good at, it hurt so much. I found myself withdrawing from life generally for a couple of weeks, my family was devastated at the hurt I was going through. My parents looked drawn. Will was beside himself not knowing how to fix this and even Rebecca was affected, not sleeping and wanting to cling to me even though she was getting older.

I needed time to repair and heal. I didn't want to go out, as I might see someone who knew what had happened and wrongly judge me. None of my team was allowed to contact me even now that hurt hugely, they had been severely warned. Some of the staff tried to speak to senior managers as they knew how unjust and false these accusations were but to no avail. Two of the team resigned and went to work in other hospitals. That's how I got my information via them.

I awoke one morning and felt that I had to fight this, so phoned Phil. He said he thought I was wasting my energy as they wouldn't let me go back. 'Go back? No way I would want to go back there but I am not going to sit back and take this. That woman needs to be stopped,' I said adamantly. 'I am going to report her for professional misconduct to the GNC.'

(General Nursing Council, the then governing body for registered nurses now known as the NMC, the Nursing and Midwifery Council.)

102

I wrote a strongly worded letter to the Director of Nursing stating that I was reporting both Mrs B J and myself to the GNC and why. Why myself? The attack is the best form of defence! I knew I was innocent and this was my best way forward. I went to see a solicitor to get advice and he was very supportive. I then reported both myself and Mrs B J to the GNC and waited.

I didn't want to look for another post, so took up agency work whilst I waited to hear from the GNC. I kept myself busy, I enrolled on a Master of Nursing Course as I needed to focus on my future. All these things kept me busy. It was four months until I heard that my case had been dismissed by the GNC with the words '*no case to answer'*.

I knew I hadn't done anything wrong, but you would not believe the relief to see this from them as my life was in their hands to allow me to continue practising.

A second letter appeared two weeks later stating more information was required as the case against Mrs B J was going to be taken forward for serious misconduct. I felt at last someone was listening to me. I received a phone call from the hospital's most senior manager asking how I was, which put me on my guard as no one worried or showed any concern before about my welfare.

He said he had been informed of me reporting one of his team for misconduct and he would like to see if I would consider dropping this by having my post reinstated and a gesture by way of payment for my distress. I was offered this but had to submit to a gagging clause and drop my case against Mrs B J. They were offering me several thousand pounds for my silence.

103

I had no hesitation. 'Absolutely not. I am taking this as far as I can and would never want to work in this hospital ever again,' I said angrily, putting the phone down. How dare they think I could be bought there was no question I needed to do this to protect others and clear my name. My determination and strength were back.

Chapter Seven

Six months had passed since my dismissal. I was almost back to being me but still not wanting to see anyone related to my old job. It left me scarred and ashamed as things like this didn't happen to "good" people or so it seemed.

I got a letter asking me to attend a hearing for Mrs BJ's misconduct. My stomach started to do somersaults and it brought flooding back all my hurt but I knew I had to do this there needed to be closure.

I attended the hearing. Phil was with me; he wanted justice almost as much as I did. I saw her walking into the building ahead of me. Her pinched face red and angry. Still carrying her trademark handbag over her crooked arm. She had someone with her I didn't recognise.

We waited outside the big room to be called in. We saw faces of hospital management going in and out, as they had been called also. No one looked my way, avoiding any eye contact. I eventually went in and it was a bit daunting. The look I was given by her could have turned me to stone, if at all possible. I was very nervous and a small man who was in the chair smiled at me and said, 'Don't worry, just think we are all friends here.' That wasn't going to happen. I had at least one enemy in the room.

The questions started. I remained composed and was concise and succinct in my answers. I was asked why I didn't like Mrs BJ and why I started a vendetta against her. This was from her representative. She was nodding during these questions. I really wanted to say what I was thinking but remained calm. I explained the relationship and how she had been since we first met. All my evidence was clearly thought out and delivered. I couldn't do anything else.

I left, not knowing what the outcome would be and slightly deflated.

Several weeks later, I had the information that she had been suspended from the register for misconduct for 18 months. She had also resigned from her post as a nursing officer before she was dismissed.

I felt exonerated but never did I want another to be removed from the register, but on this occasion, I had hoped I had prevented others from going through the pain that I had gone through. I heard that she never renewed her registration after the suspension, which was a good outcome. I hope she learnt lessons from this or it would have been all in vain on her part.

The agency work was a bit hit and miss and it wasn't always where I wanted to work, so I decided to join the nurse bank of a big teaching hospital. I spent a lot of time in an elderly care ward which I did enjoy and a permanent post came up I applied for it. I was honest in my application about what had happened without being critical of my managers and thankfully the manager interviewing was forward-thinking and non-judgemental.

I was offered the job and I was ecstatic. I worked here for two years loving the team and finishing my master's degree, getting a distinction so felt very proud of everything that had gone on. An opportunity came up for a ward sister in the medical unit where you managed all the day-care services I applied for the job and got it. I was so happy I felt that I had got back to where I needed to be. I was and always have been a determined person and nothing will put me down for long. I do also like justice and fairness, which I now felt I have.

I was sad to leave my lovely ward but we would all still be in close contact so not far away. I started the job with real enthusiasm many of the staff knew me already so that was a bonus.

I had many disciplines to manage which was a huge challenge, managing nurses was a breeze compared to managing admin staff, chiropodists, phlebotomists (people who take blood samples) and dieticians, huge staff numbers. I quickly took on a deputy who was a lovely girl but very abrupt, so frequently upset everyone. Not what I needed when staff were banging on my door, telling me they couldn't work with her. *Here we go*, I thought!

The staff were very experienced but my biggest problem was with the admin staff who were frequently off sick going home early and generally quite disruptive at times. I felt I needed a supervisor so appointed someone who had gone up the ranks and knew all the little quirks and how to get out of actually doing any work! She was a gem. Staff didn't like it and you quickly saw the real disruptive shirkers leave. Job done, we then had the team we needed.

I was duty manager often and had to go off to emergencies, looking at the bed situation to ensure we had enough for admissions and we had enough staff for safety.

Most days it was a nightmare; too many patients for so few vacant beds. Having to tell patients their admission for surgery or a long-awaited procedure was cancelled was hard. I felt for the patients so much. I hadn't seen this as much previously and the supply and demand for beds was becoming almost a crisis point.

This was a direct knock on effect of the cutting of beds and services, which was becoming more apparent and every day seemed to bring a new service under question. Surgery seemed to get the short straw as medical emergencies needed a bed and quite rightly so but not so long before the beds were there for all and we weren't faced with this stressful situation we were seeing now.

My staff continued to give challenging situations. I got a "fast bleep" (an urgent situation which requires immediate attention) from the supervisor saying that two of the clerks had returned to the department from lunch and were both under the influence of alcohol and started to argue then swinging punches!

We had really hit the buffers a new one on me. I rushed back to the department to find two young clerks screaming and pulling each other's hair and trying to murder each other or so it looked like. I waded in to pull them apart whilst instructing someone to call security, as I didn't know where this would lead.

I managed to get my frilly cap knocked off my head and dodge a few punches coming out relatively unscathed. I got them apart and had to shout amongst the din they had created, telling them to sit down and be quiet. It was exhausting!

Both of them were suspended by the duty hospital manager and neither of them returned to work after the incident. We also had our fair share of staff with illness, some extremely serious and sadly, we did lose some along the way.

I had a deep yearning in getting back into a more clinical role in the surgical speciality that I loved and the opportunity arose when a new consultant was appointed as a gastrointestinal surgeon (dealing with the gastric system); I had worked with him in a previous role and we had got on really well.

He had been in post for about six months when I sat down with him and discussed what I saw as the shortfalls in the GI (gastrointestinal) service and the need for a specialist nurse. We talked it through in detail and I was able to put forward ideas to get waiting lists down and monitor patients closely, as well as have a tight outpatient system.

I put all my ideas down in the form of a business plan and took it to the divisional manager of surgery. She looked it over and after a while slumped back in her chair and said, 'OK, sounds good, so go write the job description, write the job advert and raise the salary!'

I was a bit taken aback but agreed. By the time I got back to my office, I had planned my strategy. I got straight into writing the job description and job advert, then calling several companies who I had formed relationships with to see if I could get a sponsor for the post. It was very common for nurse specialists and indeed research posts to be sponsored by a pharmaceutical company with no strings attached so this was an ideal scenario.

I had a meeting with one of the larger pharmaceutical companies' national managers and the local rep who I knew well. I prepared my plan and how this would go.

The day arrived and they came along, briefcases in hand. The national manager was very serious and a little stern. I made it quite clear that I was looking for three years' salary for a senior nurse, but without strings to use their products or no incentivising of products. The meeting went well, I felt but had no idea how it would turn out.

Within a week, I had a call from the rep saying that I had impressed his boss and they were going to offer me a sponsorship. I was extremely proud but had no idea what the sponsorship would be. The sponsorship would basically be the company paying X amount to the hospital to pay the salary of the specialist nurse.

The letter arrived and they had offered a five-year sponsorship at a senior nurse level. This was more than I ever dreamed of. I went straight to my manager and presented the results she was more than surprised.

At this time there were so many nurses and doctors being sponsored by drug companies so it wasn't an unusual occurrence. A slight blow was that I would have to apply for the job after it was nationally advertised and compete against whoever applied. Well, I had come this far so wasn't about to give up what was essentially my job without a fight!

The job was advertised and it was agonising as I couldn't find out who I was up against until the last day. I was shortlisted and there were six other applicants, but only three who were chosen to be interviewed, so all suitable candidates. It wasn't a walk in the park. I had to work for my money with five panellists, two being consultants.

To my enormous relief, I got the job; it wasn't handed to me I deserved it and had worked hard to get it, so was determined to make it a roaring success.

I worked my two months' notice in the post I was already in but could not wait to start my new role I was beyond excited. I would have an office with my secretary and couldn't wait.

The long-awaited day arrived and I went to my new office and set about planning my week. I met with the consultants of which there were seven of them and gave them what I had done. They wanted me to take on all the surveillance Endoscopies (looking into a part of the body, usually the gut or gastrointestinal region with a flexible or sometimes rigid instrument to check for either recurrence of disease take biopsies or even initial procedures to diagnose certain conditions).

The consultants wanted to train me to perform various procedures and to be autonomous in running my own clinics and lists. I was very much up for this and felt they had complete trust in my abilities. I felt that I had now found my dream job.

I started the role and developed it with enthusiasm, seeing patients independently after full training and assessments which I welcomed and was tough on myself as I wanted it to be perfect. Very soon, I was running large lists and seeing fast-tracked patients (those with conditions that could be potentially serious and needed urgent investigation and treatment) some days it amounted to thirty-forty patients each day. I was able to diagnose and treat and refer on or back to the GP.

It was a really privileged role and I soon found I needed help as the lists of patients were enormous it was an extremely busy department. Two more consultants had been appointed so the workload grew massively.

I appointed two nurses who would be trained in some aspects of the role of a specialist nurse post. This would lift some of the workloads to enable me to concentrate fully on what was intended.

The work was so enjoyable seeing so many regular patients and meeting new ones. There were elements of sadness when you lost a patient who you had known and cared for with empathy and tenderness, lost to a dreadful disease which we could do nothing about. As one of the first nurses to be in such a post, I was regularly sought after for teaching and to join boards looking at new treatments I was seen as a KOL (key opinion leader).

Pharmaceutical reps were constantly contacting my secretary to bring information to me and to bring free "goodies" pens, lights, mugs, pads, etc., all with the drug in question or the company logos all over them. The offices were full of such things.

The consultants were regularly flown to destinations for conferences and meetings and in many cases, it was abused by the people that went as well as the pharmaceutical companies with first-class travel and five-star accommodation, the best food and free-flowing alcohol, the sky was the limit. Golfing trips, racing and yachting were not unusual and all major sporting events carried a hospitality box and everything was free.

I soon became aware of this when I too was offered the "perks of the job". It was a huge shock to me, naïve as I was that this thing was the "norm" and expected it to appear. I felt awkward and would never ask to attend meetings or conferences. It would always be offered. Getting regular patients over many years brought a close bond and, in some cases, this could be uncomfortable.

There were many times when things got this way. John used to bring me "love tapes" in the form of music that he spent hours compiling. The sultry sounds of Barry White and the like, just so he could tell me how he felt. Arthur was a man in his seventies who was another long-standing patient.

On one occasion, we had finished his consultation and he didn't get up to go. Asking him if he was all right, he produced several pieces of paper which I saw were bank statements from different accounts. He said that it was mine if I would marry him!

I caught a glance at a huge amount of money on one of them and quickly pushed it away. It made me very uncomfortable and made me feel that someone with no morals could have easily taken advantage of this situation. I had to tell him it wasn't going to happen and I thanked him for his kind offer and also advised him to be extremely careful and to talk with his family. I didn't want anyone getting the wrong idea.

I discussed this with my manager, my paranoia would always be with me and sometimes it was a bit over the top but this was one of those situations when you had to cover yourself and protect not only the patient but you.

Another very uncomfortable situation occurred when I was attending a meeting in Dublin as a speaker and part of the talk was to have a patient and partner there to give a real insight into living with a particularly long-term condition and how it affected them both physically and psychologically. David and Stella were very willing to be part of this and I explained what needed to happen.

We were flying across together and the agenda had been set out for them to stay at a hotel being wined and dined and we would all fly back the next morning. We made our way onto the plane and I sat away from them so they could have some privacy. The seat next to me was vacant and just after take-off, David came and sat next to me. I didn't think anything of it initially but soon realised he didn't want to sit with his wife and wanted to be with me.

It was a really difficult thing not to offend him or to alienate Stella but I had to be firm with him and tell him he needed to sit with her as it wasn't right; he was quite insistent initially that he wanted to talk to me. I said I had work to do so it was a good time to do it.

He did go back eventually to his seat but spent the whole time watching me. I changed my flight to come back as I didn't want to be in the same position and luckily at dinner, there were many others who talked to them both so I was able to fade into the background.

My birthday was a couple of months later and he actually turned up at my house with flowers, chocolates and a huge fruit basket on the day. I lived in the backend of nowhere and how on earth did he know it was my birthday? I was astounded, to say the least, and felt slightly violated, as this was my safe place.

Will was at home and sent him packing along with his gifts. I refused to see him again, someone else took over his management. I thought it was inappropriate he was very angry with me, I think it was more hurt at being rejected and embarrassment maybe.

Stella and David divorced a few years later but I never saw them again.

I had, whilst in my previous role as a ward sister, gained numerous higher educational certificates in the speciality. I was able to use these in my current role and this set me on an elevated level of experience from many of my colleagues. My grade at that time was reflected in this.

I had training in managing stomas (colostomy, ileostomy and urostomy mostly which is where part of all the bowel either large or small intestine or bladder is removed. This results in the patient passing either faeces or urine into a bag on the abdomen). I was able to mark patients for suitable sittings and support and teach them how to manage their bags and the skin, which can get extremely sore if not carefully looked after.

I became trained in biopsy of lesions banding and treating haemorrhoids and many surgical procedures which nurses didn't commonly perform. One of the newly appointed nurses was keen to know more so we went to see a patient who had recently had an ileostomy performed for bowel disease. He was a man in his thirties and really didn't want to have anything to do with this thing he now had.

Emily was a very quiet girl, who was a bit awkward around young men, it appeared, blushing as we were speaking. It transpired that Jakes's friends had all visited him earlier and I could smell alcohol. He had red bleary eyes to go with it. I got everything together to do a bag change with Jake. His stomach was rumbling as he said he had quite a lot of cider, which he and his friends consumed before they were thrown out by the ward sister.

I started to glove up and my bleep went off. I said to Emily to take over and remove the bag and clean the skin. I won't be long. I went to the telephone to answer the bleep. Whilst deep in conversation with the person on the other end, I heard a scream unbeknown to me, it was Emily!

I hastily finished the conversation and made my way back behind the curtains to see Emily and Jake both splattered with a dark liquid that I knew was faeces. It was dripping off of her hair and running down the front of her dress onto her shoes the smell was awful. Jake was laying there looking a bit worse for wear, he managed to escape most of it.

Emily had to go into the shower on the ward in her clothes initially, then we got her some hospital scrubs to change into. She was mortified. I quickly sorted things out and although the smell was lingering, I did see the funny side and chuckled all the way back to my office. Emily eventually got the hang of it, realising you don't hang around after a skinful of cider or curry!

During the day I frequently got called to the emergency department if a patient presented with a potentially related condition to my speciality. I always took one of the team with me for training purposes, obviously asking the patient's permission for them to be in attendance, which on most occasions they were happy with.

It was around seven in the evening when I got a bleep to see a young couple who had intense abdominal pain and some rectal bleeding (strong stomach pain and blood from the back passage in simple terms). I examined them in turn and took a medical history; it was sketchy and they were both embarrassed. They had been like this for almost two weeks but now it was becoming unbearable.

The examination was so painful for both of them but the young man, Shaun, found it excruciating. After a lot of repetitive questions, I established that this had happened during a rather excitable sex session and the overzealous use of two very large vibrators. It transpired that they both got them stuck in the rectum and thought that when they had their bowels opened, they would just "pop out".

Well, that didn't happen and in fact they worked their way inside further and stopped the bowel from working so caused a blockage. Shaun's vibrator's batteries leaked and the battery's acid burnt through his bowel. It was a surgical emergency situation, so I got him prepped for immediate surgery and organised the team.

He underwent a four-hour operation and lost more than half of his bowel and had a colostomy formed. He was very lucky to not have lost his life, as he was slowly being poisoned. Gillian, his girlfriend, also had surgery but was much luckier, just a small amount of bowel removed and no stoma. I am sure vibrators never played a part in their relationship again.

The team continued to gel and I at every opportunity gave them as much of my time as I could, as well as ensured they attended educational days and events to boost their own learning and careers. This was appreciated.

I then appointed a trainee who was incredible. She was an untrained nurse but had experience of being a health care assistant, so I wanted her to become an associate practitioner which was a relatively new role. I was happy to become her mentor and supervisor. Rachel was so reliable and knew me inside out. I didn't have to say anything she knew what I needed immediately.

Her presence seemed to upset a few staff though, as she started to get bullied by those who were working with me from the theatre. I think they felt threatened by her knowledge and ability and the fact that we were so close.

The situation became so bad with the bullying that Rachel went to Human Resources (HR) to take out a grievance for bullying and harassment. She truly was having an awful time of it. I had seen this on numerous occasions and was called as a witness. It wasn't a situation I liked it brought back too many memories for me but I knew I couldn't let it go. I want everyone to be treated fairly and with respect.

The two people in question were given written warnings, as others had seen what they were doing. They weren't allowed to work with each other again. One actually left the job and the other went to work in another department. Calm was once again restored.

There were many sad situations but when your colleagues are the ones who are the root of it. It's a different sadness.

There had been in the department next to ours a death of a consultant. He was a lovely gentleman who was a genius in his speciality. He had come to do some work in his office on the weekend, his wife and children had gone away and he had slipped and hit his head on a stoneware sink, knocking himself out and causing a major bleed to the brain. He lay undetected until Monday morning when the staff came into work and found him. This sent shockwaves through the whole hospital, just how fragile life really is.

Unfortunately, this was not the only one and we witnessed several dreadful situations with premature deaths of consultants and other members of our valuable staff. Each time something happened, we all had to pick each other back up and continue. We had no other choice but to do so. We remained professional and never let the patients see how much we were hurting but in our own groups, we grieved for our colleagues.

Day-to-day work was rewarding in itself so many of our patients were kept well and continued to be free of illness but we never dropped our guard. I was so proud of the department I worked in and of the hospital itself and looked forward to going to work every day.

I remember a reoccurring dream. I had which used to make me wake in a sweat. It was that I no longer worked in this job and I had resigned, which I knew I would never do. After discussing this with a psychologist friend, it was felt that this was because I had my other job, I loved so much, snatched away from me and I feared the same would happen in my subconscious mind. Makes sense but made me shudder at the time.

I gained more autonomy and consultants would on occasion call me and ask me to cover their clinics should they have something happen unexpectedly. This was fine with me, providing it was appropriate for patients as some could be extremely complex and only should be seen by the consultant. I also worked in the clinic alongside some of the consultants having my own lists of patients.

One particular day Mr Robertson didn't turn up to his clinic. He was always late but this was not him being late. I rang his phone and he answered, knowing it was me. He said he was called to an emergency at the private hospital and was about to go into the operating theatre. Just as he finished saying this I heard, *last call for passengers on flight EZY 3000 to Frankfurt.* The line went deadly silent and he said, I've been caught out then!

He was on his way to a medical conference and forgot to cancel his clinic. This put me in another difficult position. I wasn't going to lie, so I just said he's not coming to the clinic no explanation. That was up to him to sort out. I tried to get a registrar to cover but had a barrage of abuse from him, saying he wasn't going to be used! Well, I was used to it and had very thick skin.

We seemed to be getting busier every week the waiting lists were growing and the admin staff were stressed. It was good that we had our team of clerks, so we were tight and had each other's interests at heart as well as that of the patients.

The Pharma companies were still asking me to work with them and I did go on some amazing trips that I would never have done so if they didn't sponsor me to go.

I taught in Canada, Russia, UAE, Australia and numerous places in Europe. I ensured that my managers were aware of what I was doing and I ensured it was all in writing with read receipts for all emails. I backed everyone up to a memory stick. I was not taking any chances with anything. I was still as paranoid and my managers told me to relax I was representing the hospital as well as my profession.

It still didn't relax me to take me off of my guard. On reflection, there was no manager even remotely like Mrs BJ so why was I like this? The managers were trustworthy, in my opinion.

I was getting a little hungry for more knowledge so enrolled to become an Independent Nurse Prescriber. It was a gruelling six-month master's level course to enable me to prescribe medications and write prescriptions safely with full knowledge. I was in one of the first groups of nurses to do this course, so it was very exciting and I felt privileged.

I passed it the first time and was delighted. It made life so much easier for my role and convenient for my patients. I was also in a position to help colleagues which had a direct benefit to patients it was so worthwhile.

What would I do next? I knew I wouldn't stop there so set about looking at yet more education so I set my heart on a PhD. I would become a doctor one way or the other! I started my Professional Doctorate and loved it. My naturally inquiring mind was being fed and I was at my happiest in my personal and professional life everything was good. There were still the daily challenges but it wouldn't be normal if they weren't there and I still enjoyed meeting them head-on.

My workload was large but it didn't faze me ever. I was always there for anyone who needed me patients or staff and believe me, there were many staff who came to see me to discuss professional and personal issues. I didn't ever have a problem with that. I felt privileged that others thought me approachable and knew I was always discreet.

My teaching skills were being exercised more than ever and I was chair of many boards and also wrote in nursing journals and published several papers on various conditions and was seen as an expert. I was now in a substantive post no longer sponsored by a Pharma company and was given the title Consultant Nurse. I really felt I had achieved what I had set out to be. However, things in my personal life did have an influence on my general psychological well-being.

My beloved father was taken into the coronary care unit of the hospital I worked at and I was then on the other side of things. The unit was outstanding. All staff showed compassion and genuine care for their patients. Everyone was treated as an individual and had the highest quality of care. Everyone was calm and approachable and I felt so very proud of my profession.

My dad unfortunately took a turn for the worse and sadly passed away. I was devastated; the staff were there for me and my family they were outstanding. I wrote to the chief nurse to express how proud I was of the staff and how I hoped she would be. I will never forget those individuals and will be forever grateful to them.

I had several managers during my role and all were excellent approachable and caring even though many were not from a medical professional background. I always had the fear in the back of my mind of getting another horrendous person who potentially would destroy all my happiness. This has never left me, that awful woman left a lasting legacy with me.

Being part of the on call rota gave many challenges. I arrived in the emergency department and told yet another patient had something "stuck" in his rectum. I went along to see him and was greeted by a hostile older man who denied he had put it there, he had fallen on this thing. I found him very aggressive but think it was all down to his embarrassment, so tried to ignore his manner.

On examination, I could feel something in the rectum but had no idea what it was it was high up and I couldn't quite reach it. I suggested I have a look in with a camera so we could establish what was going on. Imagine my surprise on seeing through my camera what looked like a network of cables tightly coiled. I found the end and used an instrument to grasp it and gently pulled it. I went on for what seemed like hours.

Eventually, it all came out and I had in front of me thirty-five feet of electrical cable sat on my trolley mixed with bowel contents. Now the patient was much more sheepish and didn't say a word. He was referred to the psychiatric team as it appeared he persistently put objects into his rectum and penis. I hope he got the help he needed. I am sure it was a long road for him and he so needed support and help.

There were many "foreign objects" removed from orifices during my career and each one brought an element of surprise as who would have thought the imagination was that good?

It wasn't unusual for some of the female patients to have a crush on one of our consultants. We nicknamed him Dr Love as everyone fell for him. He certainly didn't encourage this title he was as one would say just "drop dead gorgeous".

He was a quiet mild-mannered man but did attract attention. He was constantly chaperoned because of this, as there could be misunderstanding on someone's part but not his. One of his tales were about a lady in her fifties who attended his clinic, she was very flustered and red-faced when he went to see her. She got undressed and was explaining that she rushed to get there and was a little unprepared.

As "Dr Love" went to examine her in the pelvic area, he said to her, 'Oh goodness. you shouldn't have gone to all this trouble.'

She looked puzzled at him. What he saw was glitter over all her pubic hair, it sparkled like a night sky, he said. The poor woman was mortified as what she had done was rushed home from work with no time for a shower and used her teenage daughter's Impulse Body spray all around this area but she didn't actually notice it was a glitter body spray. Both patient and doctor were very quiet after that.

I also encountered one of his groupies. He couldn't get to the clinic as was stuck in the theatre on a difficult case. I attended and a very attractive heavily made-up young woman was on the examination couch, completely naked and covered just with a sheet. As I walked in, she pulled the sheet a little higher, looking beyond me and asking where he was. I advised her that I would be seeing her and carrying out the examination.

She said, "What the fuck, I paid forty quid to get my Hollywood done just for him, this ain't on." She certainly was well groomed in that area, but her language left a little to be desired. I also explained to her that she really didn't need to do this as he was here to care for her health and wouldn't notice. She wasn't impressed with me at all!

It goes to show just how vulnerable we are as healthcare professionals in dealing with individuals who, for one reason or another, have infatuations or delusional thoughts. Many of us have encountered this and it is very alarming when it happens.

Chapter Eight

Every day the bed situation was hanging by a thread, many beds had been removed from the hospital, but the number of patients was increasing. Waiting lists for routine surgery were increasing and it wasn't unusual for a patient to be cancelled for their surgery four or five times. Not a bit acceptable but an emergency admission overtakes a routine in anyone's book due to the medical urgency.

Try telling this to the person who is in pain and has been waiting for over a year for surgery and then keep getting cancelled. Not a phone call any of us ever wanted to make but it was part of our duties.

I gained more skills and mentored many nurses who wanted to gain the skills I had honed and perfected. I was proud of what I had achieved and where I worked it was really the best place I could ever wish to work with exceptional staff and the most moral of standards.

We had the retirement of two consultants and new fresh blood came in with so much enthusiasm and knowledge the future was bright. I became part of the complete rota and worked on calls doing ward rounds and seeing emergency patients in the tertiary hospitals, also with admitting and discharging as well as learning clinical skills in surgery becoming one of only three advanced nurses in the United Kingdom.

One day on a ward round, I was writing notes at the desk after examining a patient. In walked a female junior doctor who was known to wear her designer clothes to work and was a bit of a madam. I saw her out of the corner of my eye and saw her pass me wearing white skin-tight trousers and a blue top.

As she went past me, I saw all the male patients looking more than interested. Her black thong was showing through her trousers beautifully and was totally inappropriate for work and men with catheters! I took her to one side to speak with her, advising of a code of dress; to my amazement she thought it totally acceptable "in case she got noticed by a talent scout"!

Exactly what her "talent" was, I am still to find out as it certainly wasn't medicine! She was pretty useless! The last scout we saw in the hospital was a Boy Scout so exactly how she thought this would happen was beyond me.

That same day I had to speak to yet another junior doctor who had been listening to a patient's chest, then took some blood from the patient's arm, without gloves I may add and then with the dirty syringe etc still in hand walked to the desk and took an unwrapped chocolate out of the box put it back and picked up another!

Good grief! I went to town on that one I started to feel like the local bad girl but it had to be done. He was almost shocked at what I was saying to him. Yet another, I despair! Absolutely no common sense or awareness of infection prevention and control. A waste of space in my book.

One of our consultants was an amazing surgeon but his personality left a lot to be desired. Patients loved him but the staff did not so much. He could be volatile, rude and totally obnoxious but he was the best surgeon without question. Watching him, he was precise with an obsessive (OCD) need for this in everything he did.

I was on one of our grand rounds, which involved all the multidisciplinary team members so we can look at the patient's care holistically. Mr Owen, our OCD consultant, was leading the round. In walked another consultant who was part of our department but they had always been frosty to each other. Mr Carr (the other consultant) spoke to one of the pharmacists on the round quietly and Mr Owen lost it. He pushed forward through the staff and started to shout at Mr Carr, poking his finger into his chest.

The whole ward was aghast, patients looked really uneasy and some of the staff were visibly upset by this outburst. It became so much more heated and pushing and shoving started. I looked at the others and said, 'Do something'. No one moved. I couldn't watch this going on, so got in between them saying, gentleman take this back to your office, this isn't the place. I don't know how I didn't get a slap if I am honest but it seemed to work.

They went separate ways and we carried on without Mr Owen. They spent the next six years trying to ignore each other but very difficult when they needed each other's skills. I think there was some professional jealousy with a hint of personal envy due to chalk and cheese personalities. I did wonder how I always managed to be in the wrong place at the wrong time—or maybe it was for a reason!

We had the best secretaries ever and, as a close department, we looked after each other. Clare came to work with us, a lovely girl just thirty-one but was like a rabbit caught in the headlights. When you spoke to her, she looked petrified every time for no reason. I quickly realised she was suffering from anxiety and depression. She thought everyone was out to get her and her mental health was suffering, bordering on a personality disorder.

I managed to encourage her to see her GP. I offered to go with her but she said she was fine to go. She was given medication, which seemed to help for around six months. Her mental health took a turn for the worse and her parents took her to their house after her landlord contacted them, concerned. Her mother had to call for help and Clare was admitted to a psychiatric secure unit. She was there a week or so and seemed to be doing well.

I remember getting home on a Friday evening and getting a phone call from one of the consultants saying that Clare had taken her own life whilst in the unit. We were all devastated; I sat and cried just thinking about how that poor girl must have felt. She was a beautiful soul and I think of her so often and still see her lovely face in my mind. My eyes are filling with tears as I am writing this about such a lovely lovely young woman.

We had many dramas in our small department, mostly around personal problems with staff as we all have outside lives families and general baggage but we were a family and we worked through as much as we could together. Another of our secretaries, Julie, was the slowest at everything she did. It was painful to watch her.

There was no physical or psychological reason for her being this way, it was just her. Many times, staff walked in to find her fast asleep at her desk and sat upright. When she wasn't sleeping, she was eating and all the wrong things I might add so maybe that was the reason for her persistent snoozing.

Occupational health had her fully investigated and nothing was found to be wrong, it put a huge strain on the other secretaries as they started to resent her saying she was lazy. That caused more than one argument that I stayed well and truly out of. My secretary Kathy was a dream and protected me so much and efficient wasn't the word! Just amazing.

I was on call one weekend and spent the night at the hospital, it was a Saturday night, so we had many calls from the emergency department regarding patients they wanted us to see. I had just gone to my room and got a call around two in the morning. I did have a senior registrar who was on with me for backup, in case we had to go to theatre, etc.

I went to see the patient and felt he needed to go to the theatre with an obstructed bowel. I called Rob my registrar but no answer. I paged him, still no answer, so I went off to his room, thinking he was in a really deep sleep. He was a lovely chap, quiet and conscientious fairly recently married. I got to his room and heard some noise thinking it was his TV I knocked on the door and then knocked again. He came to the door with a towel around him looking shell-shocked to see me.

His bed was right opposite the door and in that bed were two women who I identified as our medical students! I was, for once in my life, speechless and believe me, that isn't something that ever happens to me! He was trying to speak but making no sense, as he just didn't have the words. I quickly said get your pants on, we are needed in the theatre urgently and walked away.

The patient got his surgery and was fine Rob couldn't look me in the eye and couldn't really bring himself to have a normal conversation I don't think Rob ever recovered though. I am pleased to say he is still married and we actually still keep in touch, but it has never been talked about.

We had a lot of Locum (temporary posts) consultants during my time here some were fantastic some were not so much. An incident occurred when one of the clinic staff nurses came running to me saying our Locum consultant who was from an Eastern European country, can't quite remember exactly where had a patient face to the wall with his trousers round his ankles and he was "doing something" at the back.

My heart skipped a beat, getting up I wasn't sure what I would find I was, to say the least, a bit concerned. I got there to find the said doctor with his finger up the man's bottom the patient looked a bit concerned I will admit. Where he was trained, in his country, this is how the rectum is examined not like how we do it by laying the patient on their left side with knees flexed.

Phew, I was so very relieved and learnt something new that day. Another Locum, who I will name Mr Norman, was a character who seemed very up and down mood-wise. One day, he was chatty and jolly, the next withdrawn and moody. After finishing a long day, Rachel and I were walking to get the bus back to our car park, which took us through a shopping area.

In front, walking briskly, was Mr Norman looking around him but not behind so didn't see us. Coming towards him was a scruffy-looking lad who we both witnessed an exchange of items in carrier bags which were rolled up. They didn't speak and kept on walking for a short time when Mr Norman turned around to walk back in the direction he had come from. He was furious when he saw us so close to him and stormed past us, not saying a word, the parcel nowhere in sight.

The next day he was quite friendly, almost over friendly and very probing in his conversation trying to find out what we actually saw, we both thought it very obvious that's what he was doing. He said did we see his nephew who he bumped into, we said lightly that we hadn't noticed. It was an obvious cover-up but for what? We suspected drugs but how do you prove or deal with this type of situation?

It was yet another thing which was hard to prove and tell anyone about. He wasn't doing anything in work time or wasn't doing his job properly, it was a difficult issue and we even doubted what we saw but in reality, we knew what happened, so it was left at this point.

A colleague who worked in Kent said that he had had a Locum position at his hospital and there was a suspicion of drug abuse which was reported to the GMC (General Medical Council) that was ongoing. To my knowledge, he is still working and in a substantive post in the North East.

One of the things that really got to me more than anything was that one of our consultants, who initially was a gem, turned out to be so untrustworthy. I blatantly heard him lie to patients and to colleagues and this was inexcusable. It happened on so many occasions and it made me very uncomfortable to witness it. I was chairing a large national meeting and asked him to speak on one of his specialities and his surgical intervention, as he was a good surgeon.

The meeting had more than two hundred attendees. His talk was very interesting until he started to speak of his research which "he and I" had done and the findings, which were impressive but totally made up. He pulled me into this little web of deceit, encouraging me to back him up. I was mortified but could not say in this forum it was a pack of lies. I felt dreadful and I never used him again, I felt in an intangible position, which shouldn't have happened.

I had many nurses and doctors spend time with me to observe my practice and how I managed conditions. I continued to increase my knowledge and to put this into practice.

I completed my Professional Doctorate and was now Dr Maria Adams I was delighted, as was my family. I had worked so hard and everything I had achieved was on my own merit. My department didn't acknowledge my achievement, which was disappointing and maybe to this day may not even be aware I may be partly to blame for this as I didn't feel I needed to shout it from the hilltops.

There had been rumours of mergers of departments for many years but we all felt it was just that, rumour. We all had letters to tell us that this was now a serious consideration to "consolidate" several departments which were replicated across the city.

My worst nightmare was about to unfold. The merger would be that our department would be relocated to the exact place that had given me the most horrendous time in my life. I was extremely worried and felt physically sick at the thought of even stepping into that place. We had meetings, spoke to unions and looked at every possible way to stop this but it was a done deal and most of us felt we had been stabbed in the back.

The main driver was the consultant who I found to lie and be totally untrustworthy. Very disappointing, as he was quite new in his role but obviously out to make a name for himself. I found myself not sleeping and feeling panicked when I thought of going back to the hellhole that almost ruined my life. I didn't know what to think or do.

The secretaries, one by one, started getting other jobs within the current hospital just five didn't. Two consultants resigned. It left just myself and my assistant, five consultants and five secretaries who didn't want to go to other departments.

It took three years of sheer agony before we got a date to go. I wanted to meet with who would be my manager. She was Head of Nursing for surgery yet she ignored emails from me and on one occasion I went to meet her as arranged but she decided to go home early; it was a one PM meeting. I felt this was a sign of things to come and I frantically looked for another job but at my level that was almost impossible and I would have to move hundreds of miles away, something I didn't want to do and couldn't do with my family being settled and happy.

Eventually, I met with this woman who was just shocking, she was not at all welcoming, didn't want to know anything about me or my colleague and was more intent on telling me I would be having to take a reduction in my grade as I was the same as her. The jobs were so different. She was a manager with no clinical input, a completely different role. She had no idea about nurse prescribing, why was I called a "Dr"? She had absolutely no idea and was completely out of touch with current practices, etc.

I came away feeling so unhappy and afraid of what I was going into. I knew the setup at this dreadful place, my only reason for going there was my patients and my passion for the speciality.

The fateful day arrived we left what I saw as the best place ever to work. It was a day of sadness and we all went out that night and got very drunk.

The Monday came and we all went for induction, photographs, Identification badges, computer training etc. I hated it already.

We were shoved into a cupboard as an office. It was windowless narrow and depressing six of us in there. I was the only clinical person sharing with secretaries which I didn't mind and at least it was still the team together but I had no one to bounce things off. We appeared to be segregated from the rest of the team. It was really strange but very pointed out that we had been almost abandoned.

I had some abrupt emails from Lois, who was my manager; she was almost aggressive in her tone. She didn't know me but as I had not been someone she had to get appointment. She was going to make things difficult I felt. My only consolation was it wasn't just me she was like this with. It seemed to be anyone who came across from the other hospital. There was a definite "them and us" between the staff and although the nurses were nice. I always felt like an outsider.

I was the most senior nurse in this now huge department of twenty consultants but felt I was insignificant and resented by many. I was never anyone who was "in your face" or trying to make myself important. I kept a very low profile as some of the new consultants knew my worth. It was a waiting game I felt. Many of the outpatient and theatre nurses had been heard to say how valuable and knowledgeable I was, some didn't want to hear this, particularly Lois.

I kept my head down and worked my socks off. Luckily, I was able to work off-site frequently at another smaller hospital, which was a breath of fresh air. I found out that in the transfer across, a huge number of patients had "got lost in the move". Most of these patients were suffering from cancer so it was a matter of urgency these were identified but it seemed it was down to the lost patients or their GPs to come forward!

I was beside myself with anxiety over this. Despite my best efforts to raise this as a major incident, the blasé attitude was evident throughout this organisation and I found it immensely hard to deal with and whoever I spoke with couldn't provide a solution. Work became almost intolerable, not the actual day-to-day things I was used to but the organisation I was always on my guard.

I had an appraisal with Lois who, thankfully, I didn't see often so quite how she could do this. I wasn't sure. I was still getting rude and frequent emails from her, mostly her trying to make me change hours, etc., also insisting I needed to be downgraded. As part of the agreement of transfer, none of this could be changed for five years.

I kept going back to her with this, which I don't think she really liked and almost too quiet and didn't get it. I wasn't looking forward to it her attitude remained hostile and she was what I can only describe as a bully but not the same as Mrs B-J, I'm glad to say. She was like it with so many and her reputation was just shocking for this behaviour.

I was getting more and more irritated and asked her outright why she felt the need to try to bully me. She was defensive and I replied calmly but firmly, 'I am not a bully, nor will I be bullied.' I think she was taken aback by this.

I knew the deputy director of nursing from a previous job, a lovely woman who was honest and professional. I went to see her and told her the situation, showing her my emails which I had backed up. She was shocked but said I wasn't the only person who had come forward with issues with Lois, it seemed to be growing weekly. Something needed to happen.

One of the consultants who came from the other site with us was a very good-looking chap married with children and Lois was infatuated with him. I had spoken to him about what was happening and he confided in me to say that she always sat next to him in meetings and used to get as close as possible and she had even been rubbing her leg up his! Gross! He was petrified of her.

My workload was increasing, the medical staff lists were so much smaller than mine and the reason I was given was they were in training that didn't wash with me as they were left to their own devices and most were far into their training. I was expected to carry out 20–30 procedures against their 8-10. I was being run ragged. It kept me out of the department but that in one way didn't help as I never felt part of anything.

We were all moved into one huge office and hot desks were quite popular with part-time staff. There was one diva of a consultant who thought he was amazing—his own thoughts I am sure. I always went in really early, usually six-thirty AM to get as much administration done as possible before the clinic.

I had an allocated desk on certain days; as not always in the building, I sat at my desk surrounded by a mountain of paperwork, results of blood tests to go through scans, letters to sign referrals to allocate routine urgent, etc. This particularly self-opinionated and "cocky" consultant walked in around eight and said to me, why are you sitting there? I sat there yesterday!

'Well, I said I am sitting here today. It's allocated to me,' he growled.

'You had to move. I am a consultant!' He was like a petulant child.

I replied, 'I am not moving. I'm sure you can find somewhere else.' I looked away from him and he threw his bag across the large room, hitting over a plant on someone's desk.

This was not what I would expect from a professional. The professionalism of some of my 'new colleagues' was distinctly missing. I came in to hear from one of the other nurses that he had a run-in with one of the consultants he had worked with for ten years but was known for not liking male nurses.

Luke had gone to the theatre where the consultant was to question a prescription and quite rightly so. He waited to speak with him when he was between cases. They were speaking in a corridor and it became heated, the consultant grabbed Luke by the throat and threw him against the wall with some force. It was witnessed by several staff and Luke was visibly shaken up and went straight to complain to the medical director, the consultant's manager.

It was said he was under immense pressure and exceptions needed to be made! I am sure Luke would have been suspended and most likely sacked if the boot was on the other foot! It was completely dismissed and Luke was told not to speak of it again.

Luke was a senior nurse who had worked in the trust for around fifteen years and was well-liked by all this was without question "the old boys society" ganging up on anyone who wasn't another doctor. Disgusting to say the least and so very apparent in this establishment. Luke decided to move jobs, as he felt undermined and worthless.

There was also the case of a consultant who was near retirement but was known to have a drinking issue. He wasn't drinking at work; well, we didn't think he was but obviously did have more than he should every evening the smell was pungent.

He had a dreadful temper and his hands visibly shook, many a time he came into work with a cut here or a bruise there where he had fallen after drinking, his wife also a consultant just let him get on with it most likely because of his vile temper. He would throw instruments when in theatre, sometimes narrowly missing the scrub nurse or runners, they were all on edge in his presence.

He was a thoroughly unpleasant person and someone you didn't want to engage with on any level. However, on saying that he was very caring to his patients and was always on their side and they all loved him. His behaviour was intolerable and no one should have to put up with this in a workplace let alone a hospital.

Chapter Nine

Every day there were different problem notes being lost, patients not getting their follow-up appointments or investigations, long delays for surgery or even results of biopsies being lost it was never ending and so frustrating as whoever you spoke with did not seem to give a hoot.

I sincerely mean this. I was beside myself and wondered just how many patients this was actually happening to as it just wasn't my patients. There was complaint after complaint from patients, relatives and GPs but still no urgency to resolve the issues. The hospital had fantastic clinical teams throughout but the most inept managers you could possibly ever imagine.

Those of us that came across from the other hospital I was the only nurse left and just one secretary. Everyone else had gone back to other jobs. I had lost Rachel back to the previous hospital, she didn't want to leave me but hated the new place as I did. It just wasn't so easy for me to up sticks and move, I did keep trying but there was nothing for me I even tried to drop a grade but was told I was "too experienced" and it wouldn't be right.

We had so many pressures put upon us and I was working more hours than ever, it wasn't sustainable. I was a changed person, it had been noted by my close friends and family. Will was concerned seeing me go from a really happy calm person to someone who couldn't sleep was losing weight and was never at home.

Work was all consuming and sapping the life out of me. This may sound extreme but it really was. I felt I was on autopilot I dreaded going into 'that place' but still loved my work but I did feel that this was gradually sapping the love from out of me which I didn't want.

We again hit a rocky patch with one of my consultant colleagues who came across to 'the dark side' with me and was taken seriously ill and it was touch and go. I had always been very close to him as we had known each other since we were both students for a long time. It was a worrying time. It took over six months for his recovery, which we were all so grateful for before he came back to work.

I witnessed so much backstabbing amongst these twenty consultants, not all of them joined in but many did. I overheard a couple of them running down the consultant that had been unwell, mostly because he was good at what he did and very popular, jealousy is a very dangerous thing. The testosterone and chest puffing was rife and you could cut through it with a knife, almost it was like small children in the playground.

There were no female consultants and in my opinion that may have brought some of those egotistical maniacs down to earth. Things went back to how it had been previously but for only a very short time.

I was attending a training meeting in London, I remember it vividly and got a phone call from the consultant who had been so very unwell. He said that another one of our colleagues who worked at the previous hospital was in intensive care after major surgery. He wasn't expected to pull through.

I again was very close to him and had only spoken to him the day before, wishing him luck for his surgery, which was planned. He was upbeat and said he would see me soon. My head started to spin it was a real shock and such a huge blow to us all, his family was at the forefront of my mind such a shock to us all.

I couldn't concentrate on my course and was so glad when it was over.

The next morning, I got the call I didn't want to hear. He had sadly passed away at fifty years of age. I was devastated that I had lost a dear friend and an amazing surgeon. I was equally as devastated for his beautiful family who I knew so well.

Going into work on the Monday morning, there was a sense of despair and silence in the department as no one could believe what had happened to this lovely man.

I became more and more down but my work didn't suffer, neither did I stay away from work. The final straw came when I was summoned to a meeting by my then new manager Babs. Lois had been so ineffective they actually had a reorganisation in which she had to reapply for her own job and didn't get it. It was a done deal she was never going to get it! It's an easier way to get rid of someone who isn't performing without the risk of employment tribunals, etc.

Babs said as the five years were almost up I would be downgraded as I was too expensive to employ, there was no thought to the actual money I was generating through my work it was a huge amount. I questioned what the assessment

141

criteria were for this and I was informed it was being based on the other nurse specialist roles, even though I was a Nurse Consultant with both a doctorate and a master's degree who was a prescriber.

No one else in the trust possessed these qualifications or qualities so there really was nothing to be compared to. I put this to Babs, she went almost blue with rage, how dare I question her she said. We were the same grade and this was resented, I suspected it seemed to be inbred in these people as they were all so hostile and blinkered; I went on to explain I was clinical and she was managerial, so completely different.

I was very calm but I really had had enough of this shocking organisation and I use the word 'organisation' very loosely. She slammed down my file on the desk and said, "You will be downgraded we have to save money it has to be done"

I asked what would be taken out of my role to reflect the regrading. Absolutely nothing, she retorted, you will do exactly the same no compromise! At this point, I snapped and stood up saying, "Well, that is not going to happen, I can assure you of that." I then left the room and went home.

I got home and started to do our evening meal Will arrived home and immediately sensed I was not myself. We sat and talked about everything that had happened, how it evolved and how it made or changed my life. Will slumped back and said you know how you feel so do whatever makes you happy.

I rang a friend who was a senior partner in a GP surgery he had left me a message a couple of weeks previously offering me a job as an advanced practitioner. I went onto autopilot and by the time I had got off the phone, had set up a meeting for the next day with his practice manager. I went to bed but stayed awake most of the night, mulling everything over and trying to find a way around this and if there was any way I was responsible for this mess, I knew I wasn't, but I felt as though I should dissect and reflect.

The next day I met with the practice manager it was a really pleasant meeting and felt this woman was actually listening. The practice was fully aware of my capabilities and my work ethic, they had known me for almost twenty years.

I was a trainer for other nurses in a physical examinations and taught for the university. I was offered the post with the salary exactly the same but with a bonus of less hours and many other perks associated with primary care working. I came out beaming and with a sense of everything had been lifted off of my shoulders. I slept like a baby that night.

I went into the hospital the next day and typed up my notice, sending it immediately to Babs. I told my close consultant colleagues all of whom were pleading with me to reconsider but were not prepared to raise their heads above the parapet to support me. I knew it was the right thing to do.

I carried on with my work telling my regular patients of my change of role, they were devastated. I was doing my normal ten-to-twelve-hour days and about four weeks into my three-month notice when I slipped on a wet floor and injured my back and shoulder. This sent me off sick for the remainder of my notice period.

In the whole of my career, I had had less than two weeks of sickness in thirty years. I left my beloved role, which I had dedicated my working life to with not even a 'goodbye' from anyone. None of those who I saw as close colleagues who had remained at this trust contacted me.

I was saddened by this, but I don't really think I was surprised. I will add that I have been contacted for advice by several individuals since, which shows how they think and showed no consideration for how I might have felt.

Chapter Ten

I started my new role in primary care with so much enthusiasm. It was busy seeing patients with so many variable conditions every ten minutes. I loved the unpredictability and I had to use my expanded clinical judgement.

It was however frustrating when it was blatantly clear that some patients are incapable of thinking for themselves and expect everything from their GP surgery. The twenty-three-year-old man, for instance, who worked in London in the financial sector came in for an emergency appointment saying his feet are so painful he can't cope.

On taking off his shoes which looked far too big for him, I was astounded to see all his toenails had grown across the tops of his toes and were going back towards his heels! He had not cut his nails for over five years as his mother used to do it for him!

Just why I asked him do you think this is an emergency doctor's appointment. He stated, well you could cut my nails. I sent him off with a bit of a telling off and advised a chiropodist and then to do it himself. There was no reason why he couldn't.

I was amazed at how many patients booked a GP appointment for something they could easily have seen a pharmacist about and certainly do not need a doctor for. It just means taking some responsibility. Just like asking for a prescription for paracetamol when you are exempt from paying. It's not acceptable when they cost around twenty pence in a supermarket.

A young girl, early twenties, came in chewing gum and I asked her what I could do to help her. She had an itch and it was getting on her nerves, she told me. No rash, no redness, no pain, no real problem. It actually turned out to be the label on her jacket tickling her neck. Unbelievable! Not a medical problem, just common sense needed.

I was working from eight in the morning until six in the evening with two hours in the middle of the day for administration it was really busy. The whole system in primary care was bowing under the strain of yet more patients coming onto your books as more people moved into the area, more houses being built, etc. That brought with it increased waiting times and less appointments, which frustrated so many.

I experienced a different kind of stress in this role. We had frequent "lockdowns" where patients who were either drug users or violent abusers went on the rampage in the surgery. Our panic alarms were activated silently in many instances and flashed up on our computers, so we locked down our areas. It was very frightening as you could hear the mayhem going on out in the waiting area, you just hoped the police would arrive soon.

It was so frightening when the noise got closer and the fear that the door would be battered down who knew what would happen. I was new to this violence and it wasn't something I liked and felt quite vulnerable at times. My GP colleagues were very stressed and some days you would find them in tears through tiredness and frustration, no wonder so many are part-time or leaving the profession.

I was seeing so many patients and managed to have good relationships with them this built up trust and they came back to see me because they felt I listened and resolved their issues. That was what I wanted to achieve. Did I miss my previous role? I missed my patients and the work but nothing else I felt I had done the right thing.

I trained in so many new things and this was just up my street I have always had a thirst for knowledge, so I was happy. I managed a couple of nursing home's care that was enjoyable too.

I did find that the GP role was at times almost like a "lucky dip" many of them were out of their depth as the experience they had was minimal. I found myself on many occasions being asked my opinion on a patient, which is a little concerning. The surgery was a little dilapidated, very old and worn out, which made clinical work difficult. I had mouse traps under my sink cupboard as there had been sightings of the little creatures as well as a small army of cockroaches. A little unnerving especially when you were sitting quietly doing your paperwork!

My mother became unwell and had several admissions to the hospital after falls. She lived close to me and we had all the required safety devices for her. Each time she went into hospital, the emergency services were just exceptional. Gentle, kind and compassionate despite being run off of their feet. They are the true hero they really are. My mother had her 91st birthday in hospital and she was becoming weaker.

The situation on the ward was dire. Filthy floors, sweets left under the bed for days. She fell as she needed the bathroom and was on the floor for a couple of hours as no one came to her, she was calling out. She had no television, it was broken and didn't get washed until I or one of the family came in. Food and drinks were placed where she couldn't reach it and so it went on and on.

I went on holiday for a couple of weeks and on coming back went to see her, I remember having flip-flops on as it was August and hot. On walking into her room, they stuck to the filthy floor and came off my feet. I went absolutely mad and all hell broke loose. The staff were running around trying to resolve the issue, but the damage had been done it was a disgrace, infection neglect and pure filth.

The ward sister knew me and kept apologising, saying she wasn't aware it was this bad. I reminded her she needed to be aware of everything in her ward. I wasn't at all happy, this had happened.

My mother never managed to come home and passed away a week later. My heart was broken but what we were about to face would have made the situation so much worse and I don't think either of us would have coped with it.

Something none of us predicted was what happened in 2020.

Covid hit us. I remember the days leading up to the lockdown and the patients coming in with flu-like symptoms some had been away on holidays and had flown back to the UK. We weren't really aware of the severity in January and how it would affect us. I saw many patients who now on reflection could have been positive.

I just am thankful that I was on the ball with infection control and cleaning everything after each patient, which is a practice I have adopted for over twenty years and it paid off. I had always washed my hands before and after every patient to protect us both, so it wasn't an issue for me.

The prime minister televised to us in March 2020 that we would be going into a lockdown due to the dreadful death and infection rates we were experiencing. This was on a Sunday evening and I was the first clinician in for surgery on the Monday and I knew I would be inundated from the minute I stepped into the building.

I rang the practice manager in the evening to ask her what PPE (personal protection equipment) we were being supplied with, I was told we had gloves so it should be fine and this should all 'blow over' quite quickly. I was without question petrified and voiced this to her, it was dismissed as worrying too much.

I went into surgery the next day, almost quaking in my boots. I had disposable aprons, my own scrubs and my own masks which I took in with me as the surgery supplied the gloves. There was a sense of fear from the reception staff, they really didn't know what to do so I tried to explain what they needed to do to keep themselves and everyone else safe.

This was alien territory for them and there were constant questions which I didn't mind. Many of the staff were in tears and we hadn't even got started and didn't know what we were facing.

I saw more and more patients each day with symptoms of Covid but at this time we didn't have reliable tests we could use in the surgery to confirm. This did come fairly quickly but we needed it sooner rather than later. I sent many very sick patients to hospital as their breathing was deteriorating and so were they in front of my eyes.

I remember one evening that there were four emergency ambulances in our small car park because we had sick patients in several consulting rooms who needed emergency admission to the hospital. They were extremely frightened and felt very alone. We had to set up a COVID consulting area very quickly and work in that area throughout each shift; it was harrowing as any potential positive patient needed to be seen there.

The doors of the surgery were closed to patients and triage started to happen completely over the phone, that was really hard as patients want to be seen face to face so we faced verbal abuse there was also the issue that we wanted to be sure of getting a diagnosis right. There were several cases in which we heard of serious illnesses being misdiagnosed as the patients were not seen and examined. So wrong in my book, but how did we keep everyone safe? It was horrendous and my conscience was taking a massive battering.

The hospitals were filling up and I could see how my colleagues were struggling almost immediately and so much of that was fear. Would they get it? Would they take it home to their families? All these worries. I felt almost guilty as the surgeries closed the doors to patients and would only see them after triage assessment, but I heard it with my own ears 'Go to A and E'. This was so wrong. My guilt became more intense I had to go back to help at the hospital.

I contacted the hospital I worked at and loved working at for many years and they snapped my hand off. I left primary care after almost 3 years. It had helped me heal but wasn't for me.

I went back to the hospital; I won't lie I was anxious as I didn't know what lay ahead. I was working as a Consultant Nurse but in a general capacity so a bit of everything, which was a strange and unheard-of post previously. I watched how staff were driven to exhaustion and tears were shed every day by someone. Our cleaning staff and porters were crucial, but they too were under so much pressure and constantly in tears like the rest of us.

The NHS is like a well-oiled wheel and each cog makes that wheel turn we can't turn without each other. No one is more important than the next.

I saw so much suffering and death, it was almost like you were watching a scary movie at times. The emergency department was horrific people everywhere, trollies stacked up with very sick patients struggling to catch their breath, vomiting and visibly suffering, staff running around in heavy and cumbersome protective equipment exhausted no beds, running out of everything and trying their level best to stay calm and reassure the already petrified patients.

Words cannot describe how this was and how much emotional effort was being put into keeping others safe. Keeping your family safe was also always at the forefront. Showering in antiseptic before going home and going home with wet hair as you had nowhere to dry it, I could go on. Never had we ever seen such devastation in our healthcare system. We felt almost powerless.

Physically and mentally feeling exhausted wanting to sleep for a week but when getting into the safety of your own bed but not able to get images out of your head and not sleeping. I found myself getting up and trying to occupy myself with something. I remember getting up one night and baking a cake.

Will never even heard me he was tired as he was working too and was extremely worried about me and the environment I worked in, he knew I was thorough and would do everything possible to stay safe but it didn't stop his anxiety.

Days off were few and far between but you were almost on a rolling road and being carried along and felt you couldn't get off.

Every day brought a new challenge. It wasn't only the sickness you had to deal with but the emotional devastation of families, who needed to know how their loved ones were so phones were constantly ringing. You had little time to speak with families but you had to find the time to offer reassurance or to prepare them for what could be news that will turn their worlds upside down.

You also had to prop each other up and this was everyone in the team. Holding the hand in support of a senior consultant, in tears as he couldn't take any more that day, but knowing he had to pick himself up to fight another day and he would no matter what.

The public was coming out to clap for the NHS and carers on a Thursday night to show support and gratitude, the government even did it, but it wasn't what we needed. We felt quite awkward this was happening and amongst ourselves, we talked about it and wanted it to stop. The clapping eventually stopped, along with the love and support we were initially given.

We were now being abused verbally and, in many cases, physically as the frustrations of the public emerged. They were not being seen by their GP. They weren't getting their routine surgery and they were waiting for exceedingly long periods to be seen in the emergency department and in many incidences were not being allowed into the departments for various reasons. Everything was turned upside down and, frankly, a mess.

We hadn't anticipated the amount of devastation this would cause and the appalling death rate that we in the UK experienced. The government constantly changed their minds moving the goalposts, so the public was almost ignorant of what was going on.

Vaccinations rolled out but there were those who didn't want to receive the vaccine or didn't believe we had a pandemic, but it was a made-up thing. Outside of the hospital still we saw protests about masks and vaccines, the death toll continued to rise.

Lockdowns came and went we still continued to care for people no matter what. All the emergency services were still there doing the job they were trained to do and many lives were lost from these disciplines. The protestors said we got paid to do our jobs yes correct we do but so does everyone else who does a job the difference being we couldn't walk away or work from home.

You fight so hard to do the right thing it is soul-destroying when you see how many people are suffering waiting for routine surgery and being in pain and can't do even little tasks which an operation could fix. Our hospitals were overrun with COVID patients who need care, no question and we had no idea when this would ease.

Chapter Eleven

It is 29 November 2021 that I am sitting here writing the final chapters staring outside into the cold crisp day where the ice is glistening on the rooftops and I wonder just how I have got to this point and reflected on my career.

I think of all the patients whose hands I have held whilst they are taking their last breaths, the babies I have brought into this world and wondered at the joy of life, the relatives I have hugged to help with grief or I have cried with them. I remember the laughing of my staff when we were all on shift together and the joy it brought to our patients to see us happy and give the very best care to them.

Negative things like the inept and horrendous managers I encountered seem insignificant now as is the infrequent times I came across an aggressive patient or relative. This has all made me the person I am today and the nurse who knows she gave everything for her patients.

I firmly believe that I and all those who have been working in our glorious NHS during the past forty years have seen without question the best times and I believe we won't see the likes of these ever again. Training has moved to a more academic level and the practical "hands-on" learning is much less than when I was taught which has seen attitudes change sometimes not for the better.

We have the woke attitudes filtering down throughout the healthcare system and staff are now afraid to address anyone by gender, Mr/Mrs, etc. It is now gone beyond madness.

I have witnessed bullying, sexism, ageism, mistrust, fraud and so many other things which should not be happening in this environment. One thing I am pleased to say I saw nothing of was racism. This is not to say it doesn't exist but I was fortunate enough not to see it.

The NHS is made up of and relies on the excellent work of our overseas colleagues and this can be from every corner of the world, so many come to train in our highly regarded departments and they bring a huge amount of value to us and teach us new skills. Some of my good and long-standing friends are from parts of the world I hadn't even heard of and they are what make us more grounded and humbler.

We are struggling to keep staff in the NHS now, community nurses are falling in numbers, as they are exhausted and run ragged, which is having a huge knock-on effect on the hospitals and social care. People want to be in their own homes and when we had a fully functioning primary care service, this was much more a possibility, so beds were freed up in our hospitals.

Now beds are being blocked as there is no one to care for these vulnerable people once they are at home. We are in a state of crisis there is no question of that.

Our vaccination programme will continue for many years and so will this virus, so we will learn to live with this but many will die in the meantime.

I have seen so many changes over the years and watched as staffing levels have dwindled, our cupboards become more sparse, waiting lists spiralling out of control, increasing numbers of managers, more bureaucracy, deteriorating standards and many more sad facts of our current situation.

We haven't hit the winter flu season yet and today we know of a more virulent variant and still the non-mask wearers and vaccine non-believers are actively discouraging protection which is infuriating when you have personally seen the devastation and death. It is very real. Please don't ever forget that more than 1500 health and social care staff died during this pandemic. May they all rest peacefully.

As I think of all those I have worked with and the amazing people who almost helped me carve out my future, I am so very grateful for all of them. My patients have been instrumental in taking me to the level I am currently at through learning from them and being able to gain a much better understanding. It is very humbling and I feel privileged.

I am still writing and it is now October 2022 we are not isolating anymore and moving around for travel is less restrictive. We have lost our beloved Queen Elizabeth we have a new King and we are on our third prime minister of the year. Each one bringing a new Health Minister who has been ineffective at pulling the NHS back up to where it should be.

The virus still exists we are told more than one million people tested positive for Coronavirus just last week and we have to face the winter which will bring more challenges we are being told by the Department of Health that flu will be a huge problem this year we are lurching from one crisis to another.

The ambulances are now sitting outside of the emergency departments ten or more deep as they cannot transfer their sick patients into the hospital as there is physically no space. People are sitting in ambulances from what I heard yesterday for up to 15 hours until a space is free. Others are dying as ambulances aren't able to get to the homes of sick people the NHS is also dying but who is willing to save it?

Our nurses, me included, have been balloted to see if they want to take strike action. Nurses have taken to the picket lines, now junior doctors are also about to go on a three-day strike!

This is unprecedented and no nurse or doctor would leave their patients it's now in crisis and the future of our health service and that of the professions may just depend on this. We are in the worst mess we have ever seen since the NHS was founded on 5 July 1948 and if it is not handled with the care and respect it deserves, then we could see its demise— that would be a catastrophe.

I am of an age when retirement is something I need to be considering but I am not ready. I still feel the need to care for and nurture and to support my colleagues as much as I can. I am not ready to hang up my stethoscope yet I feel I still have so much more to give and I hope many can still benefit from me as I am still very willing to care for others.

Tomorrow is yet another day, never knowing what it will bring but I get up and go and give my all as I always have done and as long as I can, I will. I truly love what I do and feel I have made a difference to so many both patients and colleagues. I will always stick to my principles and will always care no one can take that from me, not ever.

I am extremely proud of what I have done and who I am and will continue as long as I can. I have named this *Behind the Mask I Wear*, as that is what I have worn throughout my career an invisible mask not allowing patients or others to see the hurt, anger, fear, frustration, distress and so many other emotions which I went through day after day. The only face I wanted others to see was that of caring, compassion and kindness no one ever knew what was truly happening and I managed to maintain this always.

I hope those of you reading this will always treasure our precious NHS staff whatever department they work in and whatever job they do. They do it because they care and want the best for those in their charge. They work as hard as they can with the resources they are given, so please remember this when you are waiting to be seen or hanging on the phone for a GP appointment. Those famous words 'Be Kind'.

Printed in Great Britain
by Amazon

53270746R00088